Vocabulary
in Context

FOR THE COMMON CORE STANDARDS

Grade
8

Table of Contents

Vocabulary in Context G8, SV 9780547625812

Introduction

Steck-Vaughn's *Vocabulary in Context* series offers parents and educators high-quality, curriculum-based products that align with the Common Core Standards for English Language Arts for grades 2–9.

Each unit in the *Vocabulary in Context* books includes:

- fiction and/or nonfiction selections, covering a wide variety of topics

- context activities, ascertaining that students understand what they have read

- vocabulary activities, challenging students to show their understanding of key vocabulary

- questions in a standardized-test format, helping prepare students for standardized exams

- word skills activities, targeting additional vocabulary words and vocabulary skills

- writing activities, providing assignments that encourage students to use the vocabulary words

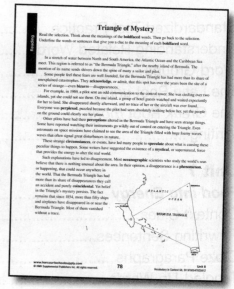

Reading selection

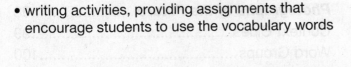

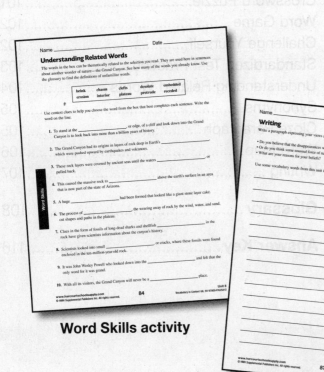

Word Skills activity

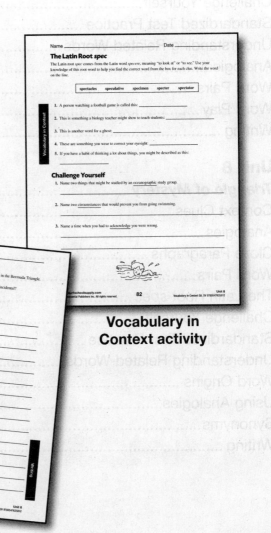

Vocabulary in Context activity

Writing activity

Vocabulary in Context G8, SV 9780547625812

Determining Meaning Through Word Analysis

Words are made up of various combinations of the following parts: prefix, suffix, base word, and root. Analysis of these parts is another way to determine an unfamiliar word's meaning.

Prefix   a word part that is added to the beginning of another word or word part
Suffix   a word part that is added to the end of another word or word part
Base Word a complete word to which a prefix and/or a suffix may be added
Root   a word part to which a prefix and/or a suffix must be added. A root cannot stand alone.

Prefixes

Prefix	Meaning	Example
a-, ab-	up, out; not; away	arise; abnormal; absent
anti-	against; prevents, cures	antiaircraft; antidote
contra-	opposed	contradict
de-	away from, off; down; reverse action of	derail; decline; defrost
dis-	lack of; not; away	distrust; dishonest; disarm
equi-	equal	equidistant
il-, im-, in-, ir-	not; in, into	illegal; investigate
inter-	between, among	international
mal-	bad	maltreat, malignant
mis-	wrong	misspell
non-	not	nonworking
post-	after in time or space	postpone
pre-	before	predawn
pro-	in favor of; forward, ahead	profamily; propel
re-	again; back	rethink; repay
semi-	half; twice in a period; partly	semicircle; semiannual; semiconscious
sub-	under, below	subzero
trans-	across; beyond	transcontinental; transcend
un-	not; reverse of	unhappy; unfasten

Vocabulary in Context G8, SV 9780547625812

Suffixes

Noun Suffixes

Suffix	Example	Suffix	Example
-ance, -ancy, -ence	vigilance, vacancy, independence	-ism	realism, federalism
-ant	commandant, occupant	-ist	geologist
-ation, -ion, -ition	imagination, inspection, recognition	-ity, -ty	sincerity, frailty
-cy	accuracy	-ment	encouragement, commitment
-eer, -er	auctioneer, manager	-ness	kindness, fondness
-hood	womanhood, brotherhood	-or	counselor
-ice	cowardice, prejudice	-ship	ownership, worship
-ician	beautician, statistician	-tude	gratitude, solitude

Adjective Suffixes

Suffix	Meaning	Example
-able, -ible	able to be	readable, convertible
-al, -ant, -ar	relating to	musical, triumphant, polar
-ate	having, full of	passionate
-ful	full of	harmful
-ic, -ish	pertaining to, like	heroic, foolish
-ive	pertaining to	descriptive
-less	without	senseless
-like, -ly	like	lifelike, scholarly
-most	at the extreme	topmost
-ous	full of	furious
-or	one who	actor
-y	state of	funny

Verb Suffixes

Suffix	Meaning	Example
-ate, -fy	to make	activate, simplify
-en, -ise, -ize	to become	strengthen, merchandise, computerize

Adverb Suffixes

Suffix	Meaning	Example
-ily, -ly	manner	happily, quickly
-ward	toward	skyward
-wise	like	clockwise

Vocabulary in Context G8, SV 9780547625812

Roots and Word Families

A word root cannot stand alone but must be combined with other word parts. A great many roots used in our language come from Greek or Latin. A single root can generate many English words.

Useful Greek Roots

Root	Meaning	Example
aster, astr	star	asterisk
auto	self, alone	autobiography
bibl, biblio	book	bibliography
bi, bio	life	biology
chron	time	chronology
cracy, crat	rule, government	democracy
gram, graph	write, draw, describe	grammar, paragraph
meter, metr	measure	barometer
neo	new	neoclassical
ortho	straight, correct	orthodontist, orthodox
phob	fear	claustrophobia
phon	sound	phonograph
psych	mind, soul, spirit	psychology
scope	see	telescope
tele	far, distant	television
therm	heat	thermometer

Useful Latin Roots

Root	Meaning	Example
capt, cept	take, have	capture, accept
cede, ceed, cess	go, yield, give way	secede, proceed, recess
dic, dict	speak, say, tell	dictate, dictionary
duc, duct	lead	introduce, conductor
fact, fect	do, make	factory, defect
ject	throw, hurl	eject, inject
mob, mot, mov	move	mobility, motion, movie
pon, pos, posit	place, put	opponent, deposit
port	carry	porter, portable
puls	throb, urge	pulsate, compulsory
scrib, script	write	prescribe, scripture
tain, ten, tent	hold	contain, tenant, attention
ven, vent	come	convention, event
vers, vert	turn	versatile, invert
vid, vis	see	video, vista
voc, vok	voice, call	vocal, invoke

The World of Mark Twain

by Howard Peet

Read the selection. Think about the meanings of the **boldfaced** words. Then go back to the selection. Underline the words or sentences that give you a clue to the meaning of each **boldfaced** word.

Mark Twain is perhaps the most famous writer in the United States, best known for his tales of boyhood, The Adventures of Tom Sawyer *and* The Adventures of Huckleberry Finn. *As this reading selection points out, however, his accomplishments and interests were quite varied.*

The name Mark Twain began as a joke. When the twenty-seven-year-old Samuel Clemens wrote a humorous article, he signed it with a phrase used by Mississippi riverboat pilots to describe water just barely deep enough for safe travel—"Mark Twain." Clemens loved to play games with his readers, and he had used odd or amusing pen names before. But this name stuck, becoming one of the most famous names in U.S. literature. The life of Samuel Clemens, or Mark Twain, proved to be as interesting and **memorable** as his writing.

He grew up during a time of **drastic** change, when the United States was being **transformed** from a **rural** nation to an industrial one. New territories, new jobs, and new opportunities gave restless dreamers such as Twain plenty of room to move. At an early age, he left his boyhood home of Hannibal, Missouri, to explore the country, ending up in places as **diverse** as Pennsylvania, Iowa, Ohio, Nevada, and California. Because of his adventurous spirit, Twain **pursued** many different careers. He was a printer, a reporter, a writer, an editor, a riverboat pilot, a second lieutenant in a group of Confederate volunteers, and a prospector for silver.

Mark Twain did not lose this **inquisitive** and restless spirit as he grew older. Besides writing books, short stories, and essays, he lectured on various subjects, traveled around the world, invested in a typesetting machine, received honorary degrees from three universities, invented a history game, learned how to ride a bicycle, and ran a publishing company. Twain's bold and busy life captured the imagination of a still young United States, and he became a rich celebrity, with admirers around the world. Even when his investment in the typesetting machine failed and his publishing company went **bankrupt**, Twain was not defeated. He just worked harder, eventually paying back every dollar he owed.

Throughout his lifetime, Twain was known for his **flamboyant** and **unique** personality. He packed lecture halls in the United States and Europe with people eager to hear his funny stories and witty comments. Even his manner of dress—the white suit, white hair, bushy mustache, and ever-present cigar or pipe—revealed a certain original **flair**, which audiences loved. Not surprisingly, the architecture and the **interiors** of his home in Hartford, Connecticut, and his study in Elmira, New York, reflect a strong, **individualistic** style. In all aspects of his life, Twain insisted on doing things his own way.

Though Twain was known for his sharp, mocking wit, he formed deep attachments to people. Certain friends, such as Ulysses S. Grant and Helen Keller, meant a great deal to him, and he helped them overcome serious financial problems. Twain was also a **devoted** family man, and several family **tragedies** affected him deeply. After his wife, Olivia ("Livy") and daughter Susy died, he never fully recovered his **emotional** health.

While his readers recognized him as the greatest **humorist** in the United States and his friends knew him as a **humanitarian**, Twain did become bitter in his last years. Perhaps because he held such high hopes for his country, he became increasingly critical of its shortcomings. His **fictional** pieces took on a darker outlook as he studied the weaknesses and failings of humanity in his stories. Ironically, the author who will always be **associated** with boyhood innocence—the wooden rafts, barefoot boys, and straw hats made famous by the stories of Tom Sawyer and Huckleberry Finn—no longer believed in the innocence of the United States. The path of Twain's life, in a sense, reflected the growth of the country itself. In his youth, he shared the unlimited confidence and energy of the young nation. In his old age, he realized that no people, no country, can live up to its dreams. Like the country he wrote about, Twain went through painful changes on his way to full maturity. But he never lost the gift for living an interesting and productive life.

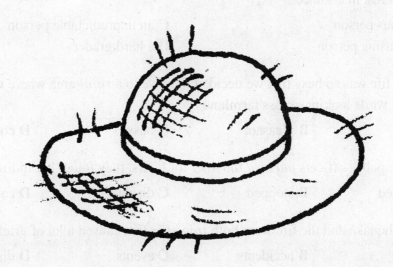

Context Clues

For each sentence write the letter of the word or phrase that is closest in meaning to the word or words in italics. Use context clues to help you choose the correct answer.

_____ 1. By showing up early for rehearsal every day, Sally proved she was a *devoted* actress.

    A unusual   B talented   C dedicated   D unpopular

_____ 2. The doctor told her patient that smoking would have *drastic* consequences for his health because of its many harmful effects.

    A enjoyable   B minor   C severe   D positive

_____ 3. Reporters often called the singer *flamboyant*, and her new dress covered entirely in diamonds and rubies proved them correct!

    A shy   B modest   C sensible   D flashy

_____ 4. The *inquisitive* child asked so many questions that I began to wonder if she would ever sleep.

    A sleepy   B curious   C quiet   D misbehaving

_____ 5. The car chase must have been the most *memorable* scene in the movie because that's the one everyone is talking about.

    A scary   B unforgettable   C long   D well-written

_____ 6. My history teacher is *a humorist* who often tells funny stories in class to make a point or spark interest in a subject.

    A a serious person   C an unpredictable person
    B an amusing person   D a hard grader

_____ 7. The city life was so busy that we decided to move to a *rural* area where we could enjoy quiet evenings while looking across farmland.

    A urban   B pleasant   C busy   D country

_____ 8. After the police officers *pursued* the thief for hours, they found her hiding in an alley.

    A followed   B stopped   C discovered   D caught

_____ 9. The earthquake and the fire were both *tragedies* that caused a lot of grief and loss.

    A losses   B accidents   C events   D disasters

_____ 10. Matt's artworks were *unique* among his peers because while his fellow artists used oil paints on canvas, Matt used bleach on black denim.

    A hard to explain   B one of a kind   C strange   D common

_____ **11.** The employees found out the restaurant owner was *bankrupt* only when they went to pick up their paychecks and were told there was no money to pay them.

    A dishonest   **B** mean   **C** stingy   **D** broke

_____ **12.** My friends are sometimes confused that I enjoy music as *diverse* as hip-hop, opera, country, and folk music.

    A alike   **B** rare   **C** common   **D** dissimilar

_____ **13.** With his expensive suits, shiny polished shoes, and slicked black hair, the politician was known more for his personal *flair* than for the substance of his speeches.

    A common sense   **B** sense of style   **C** sense of humor   **D** nonsense

_____ **14.** The excited couple *transformed* their den into a nursery in expectation of their first child.

    A built   **B** exchanged   **C** converted   **D** left

_____ **15.** The artist had an *individualistic* style, unlike anything that had ever been seen before, and many galleries refused to show his work.

    A ridiculous   **B** nonconforming   **C** common   **D** modern

_____ **16.** It was impossible to tell from the outsides of the simple brick houses that their *interiors* were decorated in brilliant colors.

    A backyards   **B** insides   **C** roofs   **D** bathrooms

_____ **17.** The detective's discovery that the villain was *associated with* many art thieves explained how she was able to steal the highly guarded statue.

    A connected to   **B** hired by   **C** different from   **D** disliked by

_____ **18.** Despite rumors in newspapers that the novel was based on a famous politician and her family, the author insisted the book was *fictional*.

    A true   **B** imaginary   **C** unbiased   **D** copied

_____ **19.** Although the actor was often called selfish in his youth, he became an accomplished *humanitarian*, raising money for programs aiding children and invalids at home and abroad.

    A person who works in the arts   **C** person who promotes human welfare
    B person who cares only for himself   **D** person who makes a lot of money

_____ **20.** Psychologists believe that learning to talk about how you feel can help you develop *emotional* health.

    A related to ideas   **B** related to actions   **C** related to talking   **D** related to feelings

Vocabulary in Context

Word Maze

All the words in the box are hidden in the maze. The words are arranged forward, backward, up, down, and diagonally. Circle each word as you find it and cross the word off the list. Different words may overlap and use the same letter.

associate	bankrupt	devoted	diverse	drastic
emotional	fictional	flair	flamboyant	humanitarian
humorist	individualistic	inquisitive	interiors	memorable
pursue	rural	tragedy	transform	unique

```
I  N  T  E  R  I  O  R  S  B  H  I  M  F
O  N  Y  D  E  G  A  R  T  A  U  N  R  L
E  U  Q  I  N  U  Z  P  S  N  M  D  O  A
X  H  Z  U  G  M  U  I  E  K  O  I  F  I
C  U  G  J  I  R  J  O  V  R  R  R  V  S  R
D  M  F  X  K  S  W  X  N  U  I  I  N  A
R  A  L  N  H  J  I  K  I  P  S  D  A  M
A  N  A  R  C  H  I  T  E  T  T  U  R  E
S  I  M  L  U  S  O  R  I  L  X  A  T  M
T  T  B  P  U  R  S  U  E  V  K  L  D  O
I  A  O  R  T  U  A  W  M  J  E  I  E  R
C  R  Y  N  W  C  B  L  A  C  J  S  T  A
O  I  A  S  S  O  C  I  A  T  E  T  O  B
L  A  N  O  I  T  C  I  F  G  X  I  V  L
L  N  T  D  I  V  E  R  S  E  H  C  E  E
Y  Z  L  A  N  O  I  T  O  M  E  C  D  G
```

Standardized Test Practice

Circle the letter of the word that is closest in meaning to the capitalized word.

TIP

Always read all the answer choices. Many choices may seem correct. Only one answer choice has the same meaning as the capitalized word.

Vocabulary in Context

1. FLAMBOYANT
   A showy   C floatable
   B fiery   D boyish

2. INQUISITIVE
   A poor   C insides
   B curious   D superior

3. RURAL
   A urban   C country
   B suburban   D grassy

4. UNIQUE
   A unequaled   C unfinished
   B united   D excellent

5. TRAGEDIES
   A changes   C nobilities
   B blessings   D misfortunes

6. PURSUE
   A read   C run
   B chase   D arrest

7. BANKRUPT
   A penniless   C cowardly
   B lazy   D trustworthy

8. DRASTIC
   A modest   C funny
   B foolish   D severe

9. DIVERSE
   A divided   C varied
   B difficult   D poetic

10. ASSOCIATED
    A connected   C separated
    B sensed   D assured

Circle the letter of the word that is the correct answer.

11. The word *flair* means
    A wealth.   B good looks.   C style.   D balance.

12. The word *humorist* means a person who is
    A dishonest.   B funny.   C friendly.   D even-tempered.

13. The word *individualistic* means
    A unkind.   B lonely.   C common.   D nonconforming.

14. The word *transformed* means
    A made.   B traveled.   C converted.   D harmed.

Understanding Related Words

The words in the box are closely related to the vocabulary words. See how many of the words you already know. Use the glossary to find the definitions of unfamiliar words.

association	bankruptcy	devotion	diversity	emotion
exterior	fiction	humorous	individualist	inquire
inquiry	memorize	nonfiction	pursuit	require
tragic	transformation	unemotional	uninquisitive	uniqueness

Write the word from the box that best completes the meaning of the sentence.

1. Jason called the movie theater to _____ when the show would begin.

2. The most _____ part of the skit was when the clown threw the pie.

3. I have to _____ the capitals of the fifty states for a test.

4. Because of her _____ to science over many years, Marie Curie made important discoveries.

5. The police _____ is sponsoring a fair to raise money.

6. Even though the _____ of the house was run-down and shabby, the interior was neat and clean.

7. The _____ of a hobby takes time and patience.

8. Although some novels include real-life occurrences, other novels are works of

   pure _____.

9. The _____ of this vase makes it very valuable.

10. Some people show their feelings easily, but others find it difficult to express

    _____.

Word Skills

Multiple-Meaning Words

Write the letter of the situation that best shows the meaning of the **boldfaced** word.

_____ 1. **emotion**

  A The judge told the jury to listen carefully to the testimony.

  B The little boy cried uncontrollably when he couldn't find his parents.

  C Rene worked through the problems on the math test.

_____ 2. **inquire**

  A Carly loved to ask her teacher questions.

  B The musician sat quietly and listened to the recording.

  C Benetta's mother jogs five miles a day.

_____ 3. **humorous**

  A Few people could understand the lecture.

  B The writer's amusing stories entertained readers across the country.

  C The singer's lack of practice resulted in a poor performance.

_____ 4. **individualist**

  A The two sisters sometimes dressed exactly alike.

  B The adolescent would do anything to fit in with the crowd.

  C The designer never imitated others; instead, she developed her own style.

_____ 5. **devotion**

  A The cows search for grass in the pasture.

  B Emilia exercises for two hours every day.

  C Hans tries hard only when he is in the right mood.

_____ 6. **transformation**

  A Irrigation turned the desert into productive cropland.

  B No one expected any change in policy this year.

  C The uniforms were baggy and uncomfortable.

Word Skills

Name _____   Date _____

The Prefixes *un-* and *non-*

The common prefixes *un-* and *non-* usually mean "not" or "opposite of." For example, *unafraid* means "not afraid." You can create the antonyms of many words simply by adding the prefix *un-* or *non-* to them.

Match each word on the left with its definition on the right. Write the appropriate letter on each line.

_____ **1.** unemotional   **A** forgettable

_____ **2.** nonhumorous   **B** without feeling

_____ **3.** unmemorable   **C** not funny

_____ **4.** nonfiction   **D** not curious

_____ **5.** uninquisitive   **E** writing that is true

The Suffix *-ist*

The suffix *-ist* means "a person who does, makes, or practices" or "a person who is skilled in or an expert in."

In each of the following sentences, there is a blank line followed by a word in parentheses. Add *-ist* to the word and write it on the line. Some words will need other spelling changes, which you may want to check in a dictionary.

1. An _____ (individual) is a person who insists on living a life that does not imitate others' lives.

2. The talented _____ (guitar) played a three-hour concert last night.

3. You would expect a _____ (biology) to be an expert in the study of plant and animal life.

4. A _____ (psychology) should possess a clear understanding of human behavior and motivations.

5. The _____ (revolution) would not be satisfied with promises of gradual changes.

Word Skills

Name _____ Date _____

Writing

Write a short account of a memorable event from your childhood. In order to make your account lively and dramatic, describe the background and the characters fully. End by reflecting on what you learned from the event.

• What happened during the event?
• Where did it take place?
• How did the event end?
• What did you learn from the memorable event?

Be sure to use some of the vocabulary words from this unit in your writing.

_____

_____

_____

_____

_____

_____

_____

_____

_____

_____

_____

_____

_____

_____

_____

Unit 1
Vocabulary in Context G8, SV 9780547625812

The Navy's Computer Age

by Howard Peet

Read the selection. Think about the meanings of the **boldfaced** words. Then go back to the selection. Underline the words or sentences that give you a clue to the meaning of each **boldfaced** word.

The clock in the office of retired U.S. Rear Admiral Grace Murray Hopper ran **counterclockwise**. In other words, it ran backward instead of forward. But it told perfectly good time. Rear Admiral Hopper kept the clock as a reminder to others that the ways things have always been done isn't the only way, that change can be **constructive**.

Rear Admiral Hopper spent most of her adult life in a field—computer science—that changed the way many things were done. Hopper was an **educator** who taught mathematics before joining the Navy in 1943. Because of her background, she was asked to join the team that built the nation's first computer. This computer was the **experimental** Mark I, designed to test what computers could do.

At first Hopper did not feel **adequately** prepared for the job of computer building. Then she realized that no one really had the experience for the task. The 1940s and 1950s were the era of the radio tube. **Transistors**, the tiny devices that took the place of tubes, had not been invented. Neither had the computer languages we use today. Computers talked through a system of electronic blips.

Hopper found that working with this computer code was boring and time-consuming. Her **initiative**, or willingness to create new things, led to the development of COBOL. Called Common Business Oriented Language, it became a popular computer language.

Programmers who designed programs for business **application**, or use, liked COBOL because it used simple words like *read* and *write* that even computer novices could understand. One thing it would not do, however, was process highly complicated mathematical formulas that featured many **variables**, or changing numbers. For that kind of task, a different language, called FORTRAN, could be used.

The success of the Mark I led to other computer assignments for Rear Admiral Hopper. In fact, she worked on everything from military programs to programs for issuing paychecks to Navy personnel. Throughout her career, she saw computers get faster and faster. Today, answers are computed in a **split second**, or in an instant. Rear Admiral Hopper predicted that one day, computers would reach the speed of light.

MARK 1 COMPUTER

Context Clues

Meanings for the vocabulary words are given below. Go back to the selection and read each sentence that contains a vocabulary word. If you still cannot tell the meaning, look for clues in the sentences that come before and after the one with the vocabulary word. Write each word from the box beside its meaning.

application	educator	counterclockwise	variables	transistors
split second	experimental	initiative	constructive	adequately

1. _____ : sufficiently; well enough

2. _____ : instant; very short period of time

3. _____ : in a direction opposite of the normal movement of a clock

4. _____ : teacher

5. _____ : having to do with ideas that are being tested; not yet proven

6. _____ : changing numbers; symbols that represent things that can change

7. _____ : the act of putting to use

8. _____ : willingness to try new things; ambition to take the lead

9. _____ : electronic devices that take the place of radio tubes

10. _____ : helpful

Vocabulary in Context

Name _____ Date _____

Synonyms and Antonyms

Synonyms are words that have similar meanings, while antonyms are words that have opposite meanings. Look at each of the words listed below. If they are synonyms, put a (✓) in the Synonyms column. If they are antonyms, put a (✓) in the Antonyms column.

	Antonyms	Synonyms
1. constructive—destructive	_____	_____
2. adequately—sufficiently	_____	_____
3. educator—teacher	_____	_____
4. variables—constants	_____	_____
5. application—use	_____	_____
6. experimental—proven	_____	_____
7. counterclockwise—clockwise	_____	_____

Cloze Paragraphs

Use the words in the box to complete the passage. Then reread the passage to be sure it makes sense.

split second	educator	initiative	counterclockwise	constructive

Nicolás and Anne watched as the computer flashed the first screen of the game in a

(1) _____, faster than either of them had expected. Slowly an arrow moved in

a (2) _____ direction until it came to a halt.

Nicolás took the (3) _____ by attempting to answer the question

the arrow pointed to. He did not know the answer to his question and asked Anne for some

(4) _____ tips on how to play the game better. Anne wanted to win but decided

to help Nicolás by taking the role of a helpful (5) _____.

Crossword Puzzle

Use the words in the box and the clues to complete the crossword puzzle.

application	educator	variables	constructive	transistors
initiative	adequately	experimental	split second	

Across

2. unproven
4. use
6. helpful
7. ambition to take the lead
8. instant

Down

1. electronic devices
2. teacher
3. sufficiently
5. symbols that represent things that can change

Name _____ Date _____

Word Game

Read each clue. Then write the word from the box that fits the clue.

initiative	experimental	constructive	counterclockwise
split second	educator	transistors	

1. You could find these inside your radio. _____

2. If you plan to pursue a career as a teacher, this is what you want to be. _____

3. If you mow yards all summer to save money, you are showing this. _____

4. A new drug that has not yet been tested on patients would be called this.

   _____

5. If something happens so quickly you don't even notice it happened at all, you might say it

   happened in this. _____

6. If you give helpful feedback on your friend's paper, your friend might say your feedback is this.

   _____

7. If the hands on your clock move in the opposite direction from everyone else's, they move like this.

   _____

Challenge Yourself

1. Name two things you can do in a split second.

   _____

2. Name two things you can do adequately.

   _____

3. Name two educators you know.

   _____

Vocabulary in Context

Name _____ Date _____

Standardized Test Practice

Choose the word or words that best take the place of the italicized word or words. Circle the letter of the correct answer.

TIP

Before you choose your answer, try reading the sentence, replacing the italicized word with each answer choice. This will help you choose an answer that makes sense.

1. Stephanie's suggestions were *constructive*. They made the fair a success.

   A destructive   **C** possessive

   B unclear   **D** helpful

2. He was *adequately* prepared. Therefore, he did well on the test.

   A sufficiently   **C** poorly

   B carelessly   **D** openly

3. This car is *experimental*. We have not yet confirmed its capabilities.

   A self-powered   **C** unproven

   B miniscule   **D** outdoor

4. Sonia wants to be an *educator*. She wants to work with children.

   A teacher   **C** trustee

   B curator   **D** scientist

5. The *transistors* in the radio will need to be repaired by a professional.

   A supplies   **C** sinks

   B electronic devices   **D** broken glass

6. It happened in *a split second*. I blinked and missed the entire event.

   A an instant   **C** a time

   B an hour   **D** a possibility

7. What is the *application* of this product? I need to know what it does.

   A course   **C** use

   B language   **D** meeting

8. Manuel has *initiative*. It helps him to do well on a new job.

   A mistrust   **C** laziness

   B courage   **D** ambition

9. Check the *variables* in the formula. Write down any differences you discover.

   A wires   **C** currents

   B magnets   **D** changing numbers

10. The dancers moved *counterclockwise*. Then they moved the other way.

    A in the opposite direction of a clock's hand

    B carefully

    C in a straight line

    D rapidly

Name _____ Date _____

Understanding Related Words

The words in the box can be related to computers and technology. See how many of the words you already know. Use the glossary to find the definitions of unfamiliar words.

automated	contemporary	convenience	integrates	modem
outmoded	replacements	revolutionized	simplifying	utility

Write each word from the box beside its meaning.

1. _____ : operated, controlled, or worked by a machine

2. _____ : usefulness

3. _____ : a device for transmitting data from one computer to another

4. _____ : changed greatly

5. _____ : things that take the place of other things

6. _____ : belonging to today

7. _____ : brings parts together into a whole

8. _____ : out-of-date; no longer useful or acceptable

9. _____ : freedom from difficulty

10. _____ : making easier

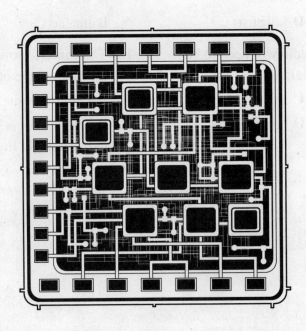

Vocabulary in Context G8, SV 9780547625812

Word Skills

Name _____ Date _____

Word Origins

Knowing the origin of a word can help you understand its meaning. Read each word origin. Then write each word from the box next to its origin.

| integrates | contemporary | utility | simplifying | automated | convenience |

1. from the Latin *integer*, meaning "whole": _____

2. from the Greek *automatos*, meaning "self-acting": _____

3. from the French *simplifier*, meaning "to make simple": _____

4. from the Latin *comtemporarius*, meaning "same time": _____

5. from the Middle English *utilite*, meaning "usefulness": _____

6. from the Latin *convenire*, meaning "to be suitable": _____

Word Groups

As you read each pair of words, think about how they are alike. Write the vocabulary word from the box that best completes each group.

| replacements | contemporary | convenience | utility | outmoded | revolutionized |

1. modern, current, _____

2. usefulness, practicality, _____

3. substitutes, alternatives, _____

4. ease, freedom, _____

5. old-fashioned, dated, _____

6. changed, transformed, _____

Vocabulary in Context G8, SV 9780547625812

Name _____ Date _____

Analogies

An **analogy** compares two pairs of words. The relationship between the first pair of words is the same as the relationship between the second pair of words. For example: *Quick* is to *fast* as *loud* is to *noisy*. Or an analogy may show that one thing is a type or kind of another thing. For example: *Diamond* is to *jewel* as *iron* is to *metal*.

Use the vocabulary words from the box to complete the following analogies.

outmoded	replacements	modem	revolutionized
integrates	convenience	automated	contemporary

1. *Stopped* is to *halted* as _____ is to *transformed*.

2. *Problem* is to *solution* as _____ is to *hardship*.

3. *Ancient* is to *past* as _____ is to *today*.

4. *Rich* is to *wealthy* as _____ is to *out-of-date*.

5. *Wheel* is to *transportation* as _____ is to *communication*.

6. *Arrives* is to *departs* as _____ is to *separates*.

7. *Taxi* is to *cab* as _____ is to *substitutes*.

8. *Arranged* is to *grouped* as _____ is to *mechanized*.

Word Pairs

Words with similar parts may have related meanings. Study each word pair. Think about how the meanings of the words are alike. Check the meanings in the dictionary. Then write a sentence for each word.

1. utilize—utility

_____

_____

2. simple—simplifying

_____

_____

3. automatic—automated

_____

_____

Vocabulary in Context G8, SV 9780547625812

Word Skills

Writing

Rear Admiral Hopper kept a clock running counterclockwise as a reminder that the way things have been done isn't necessarily the only way. The clock is also a reminder that change can be constructive.

Write a paragraph telling your ideas for some kind of constructive change.

• What idea do you have for changing the way something is done?
• Would you change something in your school, town, or somewhere else?
• What problems would the change solve?

Include examples and be sure to use some of the vocabulary words from this unit in your description.

_____

_____

_____

_____

_____

_____

_____

_____

_____

_____

_____

_____

_____

_____

_____

_____

Moving Oil and Gas

by Howard Peet

Read the selection. Think about the meanings of the **boldfaced** words. Then go back to the selection. Underline the words or sentences that give you a clue to the meaning of each **boldfaced** word.

How much do you know about pipelines? You may have heard of those that carry oil in places like Alaska, but you probably do not know how widespread the pipeline has become in today's world. From the following selection you will learn more about this method of moving goods and how it supplies a nation with fuel and energy.

Somewhere underground, every day, around the clock, huge **volumes** of crude oil products and natural gas are moving, carried by a **system** that works so silently and **efficiently** that you may not even be aware of its **existence**. What has made all this possible is the development of the pipeline.

Moving substances over distances through pipes is an old idea. The ancient Romans used pipelines— and the force of gravity—to supply cities with water. Their system worked only if water could flow downward toward its destination. It was in sixteenth-century London that people first thought of putting pumps in pipelines to keep their water flowing. In 1865, the world's first successful oil pipeline carried eight hundred barrels of oil a day from an oil field in Pennsylvania to a railroad five miles away. A few years later, a wooden pipeline carried natural gas 25 miles to customers in Rochester, New York. In 1879, a pipeline began carrying ten thousand barrels of oil a day from Coryville to Williamsport, Pennsylvania, a distance of 110 miles.

In the 1920s, a **technological innovation** took place that eventually made it possible for gas and oil companies to build pipelines thousands of miles long. This was the development of seamless, electrically welded pipe that was strong enough to move much greater quantities of goods than ever before. The **diameter** of an oil pipeline these days is often forty inches; in a natural gas pipeline it can be four feet or more. As a result of the improved technology, pipelines became the most **economical** way to transport fuel. It is now much cheaper, for example, to send a gallon of oil from Texas to New York than to send a postcard the same distance.

Oil must make a long journey from where it comes out of the ground to where it is **consumed**, and pipelines are needed for at least part of that journey. First the natural gas must be separated from the crude oil and sent off to be processed and marketed. Then the crude oil is transported, perhaps by a tanker at a waterside **terminal**. Eventually the oil goes to a **refinery**, a plant that converts crude oil into various useful products, such as gasoline, kerosene, aviation fuel, or heating oil. Finally these products must be transported to markets by tanker, truck, railroad tank car, or pipeline.

A large pipeline is a kind of **artery** for the nation—it is able to carry more than a million barrels of oil a day. Today, a network of pipelines with a total length of about 227,000 miles carries petroleum products to every part of the United States. At the same time, natural gas is being moved in a million-mile network. Pipelines are also being used to ship many things besides gas, oil, and water. Now you can send just about anything from coal to food through a tube. In fact, pipelines rank third among types of **domestic** freight carriers in the amount of tonnage they handle.

Pipelines are normally buried about three feet underground. To meet safety standards, they must be put through careful testing **procedures**. Valves are installed along the line in order to limit and **isolate** any damage that might result from an accident. Since **corrosion** can be a problem, pipelines are often protected by the **application** of a low-voltage electric current that keeps corrosion away almost indefinitely. Although most pipelines are made of steel, plastic pipes are also used; for example, plastic lines are used for the **injection** of water into the ground to force oil and gas to the surface.

Pipelines go almost anywhere—through swamps and forests, across deserts, under rivers and lakes, and over mountain ranges. Sometimes ditches must be dug through solid rock; in some cases, the pipelines may lie on the surface. The builders of the Trans-Alaska Pipeline, which taps the oil reserves of Alaska's North Slope region, had to **contend** with a number of **obstacles** but overcame them all. In its 800-mile course, the pipeline crosses twenty large rivers, three hundred streams, three mountain ranges, and nearly 400 miles of frozen land.

The next time you use natural gas or an oil product—whether to fuel a motor, cook a meal, or heat a building—think about where the gas or oil comes from and the distance it travels. Also consider how pipelines contribute to the quality and convenience of your daily life.

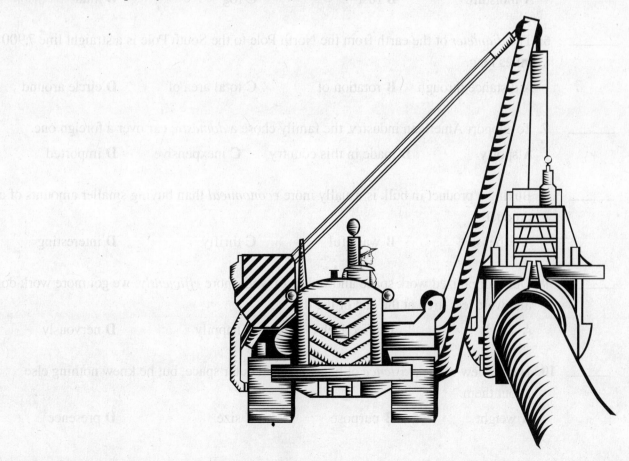

Vocabulary in Context G8, SV 9780547625812

Name _____ Date _____

Context Clues

For each sentence write the letter of the word or phrase that is closest in meaning to the word or words in italics. Use context clues to help you choose the correct answer.

_____ 1. The *application* of sunblock lotion protects the skin from harmful rays.

    A removal   B putting on   C storage   D washing off

_____ 2. The heart specialist said the patient had a clogged *artery*, which dangerously reduced the flow of blood.

    A windpipe   B nerve ending   C blood vessel   D sinus cavity

_____ 3. Fresh fruit must be shipped to the city quickly so it can be *consumed* before it spoils.

    A grown   B wasted   C eaten   D thrown away

_____ 4. It was bad enough facing freezing temperatures and bitter winds, but we had to *contend with* deep snowdrifts that blocked the trail.

    A struggle against   B enjoy   C take advantage of   D describe

_____ 5. The *corrosion* caused by the salty sea spray ate a hole in the front panel of our car.

    A moisture   B rust   C fog   D mud

_____ 6. The *diameter* of the earth from the North Pole to the South Pole is a straight line 7,900 miles long.

    A distance through   B rotation of   C total area of   D circle around

_____ 7. To support American industry, the family chose a *domestic* car over a foreign one.

    A sporty   B made in this country   C inexpensive   D imported

_____ 8. Buying a product in bulk is usually more *economical* than buying smaller amounts of a product.

    A expensive   B wasteful   C thrifty   D interesting

_____ 9. Our reorganized work space allowed us to work more *efficiently*: we got more work done and were less tired at the end of the day.

    A slowly   B effectively   C happily   D nervously

_____ 10. Hank knew of the *existence* of black holes in outer space, but he knew nothing else about them.

    A weight   B purpose   C size   D presence

_____ **11.** Tony hoped the *injection* of humor into his speech would give his audience a few laughs and improve his grade.

    A lack   **B** introduction   **C** organization   **D** dismissal

_____ **12.** The use of concrete was an important *innovation* that made it possible for the Romans, beginning around 200 B.C., to construct much larger buildings.

    A disadvantage   **B** new method   **C** old tradition   **D** problem

_____ **13.** The dog trainer told us to *isolate* our puppy when she misbehaved, so we put her in a room by herself for three minutes.

    A set apart   **B** scold   **C** reward   **D** confuse

_____ **14.** Nora found that her youth and inexperience were *obstacles* in her search for work. After two months, she was still looking for a job.

    A benefits   **B** barriers   **C** responsibilities   **D** agents

_____ **15.** The principal told Li that the usual *procedure* for adding a class was to talk to the teacher first.

    A method   **B** excuse   **C** reason   **D** expression

_____ **16.** The raw sugar was shipped to a *refinery*, where it was made into the pure white product we buy at the supermarket.

    A warehouse   **B** market   **C** shipping station   **D** processing plant

_____ **17.** River transportation is important in Paraguay because the country lacks a good *system* of roads or railroads.

    A position   **B** network   **C** example   **D** idea

_____ **18.** The developing country hoped to receive *technological* assistance from developed nations in the form of computers, machinery, factory equipment, and telephone systems.

    A scientific and industrial   **B** educational   **C** political   **D** health and public safety

_____ **19.** When our train finally arrived at the *terminal*, we knew the long journey was over.

    A first signal   **C** middle of the crossing
    B beginning of the track   **D** end of the line

_____ **20.** The governor received huge *volumes* of protest mail after she announced a new tax increase.

    A reductions   **B** quantities   **C** delays   **D** announcements

Vocabulary in Context

        Vocabulary in Context G8, SV 9780547625812

Name _____ Date _____

Word Maze

All the words in the box are hidden in the maze. The words are arranged forward, backward, up, down, and diagonally. Circle each word as you find it and cross the word off the list. Different words may overlap and use the same letter.

application	artery	consume	contend	corrosion
diameter	domestic	economical	efficiently	existence
injection	innovation	isolate	obstacles	procedures
refinery	system	technological	terminal	volumes

```
L  A  R  T  E  R  Y  K  L  G  H  P  E  I
C  O  P  R  O  C  E  D  U  R  E  S  M  N
O  B  J  P  Z  X  W  T  J  D  I  I  U  N
R  S  V  O  L  U  M  E  S  F  N  S  S  O
R  T  R  E  F  I  N  E  R  Y  J  O  N  V
O  A  Z  Y  J  R  C  G  H  D  E  L  O  A
S  C  R  E  T  E  M  A  I  D  C  A  C  T
I  L  A  N  I  M  R  E  T  V  T  T  O  I
O  E  Z  M  E  T  S  Y  S  I  I  E  N  O
N  S  D  O  M  E  S  T  I  C  O  O  T  N
B  E  C  N  E  T  S  I  X  E  N  N  E  R
C  E  C  O  N  O  M  I  C  A  L  Z  N  A
D  Y  L  T  N  E  I  C  I  F  F  E  D  X
T  E  C  H  N  O  L  O  G  I  C  A  L  Z
```

Standardized Test Practice

Choose the letter of the word that is closest in meaning to the capitalized word. Circle the letter of the best answer.

TIP

Remember that the correct choice is the one with the closest meaning to the capitalized word. If you aren't sure of the answer, try crossing out the choices you know are incorrect. Then, see which word out of the ones left has the closest meaning.

1. ECONOMICAL
   A wealthy   C inquisitive
   B emotional   D thrifty

2. EFFICIENTLY
   A skillfully   C courteously
   B loosely   D watchfully

3. OBSTACLES
   A agents   C barriers
   B accidents   D reminders

4. INJECTION
   A disease   C insertion
   B replacement   D tool

5. INNOVATION
   A identification C invention
   B declaration   D benefit

6. ISOLATE
   A separate   C invite
   B devote   D punish

7. CONTEND
   A express   C battle
   B satisfy   D devote

8. APPLICATION
   A use   C expression
   B position   D surge

9. CORROSION
   A rust   C moisture
   B illusion   D dirt

10. DOMESTIC
    A foreign   C outside
    B of this country D of this Earth

11. PROCEDURES
    A excuses   C efforts
    B experiments   D methods

12. REFINERY
    A nice things   C store
    B processing plant D storage facility

Circle the letter of the word that correctly completes the sentence.

13. The word *diameter* means a straight line passing through a
    A triangle.   B square.   C box.   D circle.

14. The word *technological* means related to
    A music.   B arts and humanities.   C language.   D science and industry.

Vocabulary in Context

Understanding Related Words

The words in the box are closely related to the vocabulary words. See how many of the words you already know. Use the glossary to find the definitions of unfamiliar words.

apply	arterial	consumer	contention	corrosive
efficiency	isolation	proceed	refine	systematic

Write the word from the box that is most clearly related to the situation described by the sentence or group of sentences.

_____ 1. As the measles outbreak worsened, college officials set aside a special dorm for sick students to keep them away from healthy students.

_____ 2. The search for the missing child was thorough. Volunteers were organized into three groups. Twenty searchers combed the woods, ten more waded down the stream, and five people questioned other campers and hikers.

_____ 3. Many businesses investigate customers' likes and dislikes and try to predict what products will be purchased.

_____ 4. Gold found in nature is often mixed with other metals in the form of ore. Special equipment is needed to separate the gold from other metals and purify it.

_____ 5. Getting accepted by a college requires filling out a long form, writing an essay about yourself, and collecting letters of recommendation from your teachers.

_____ 6. When mixed with water, the salt used to melt ice on many northern roads eats away at a car's finish and may cause the bottom of the car to rust.

_____ 7. The color green in any traffic signal means one thing: traffic can move ahead.

_____ 8. Anna firmly believes pit bulls do not belong in town, and she will argue her point with anyone who will listen.

_____ 9. In a large city, engineers identify certain streets that carry most of the city traffic and build them wide so they can have as many as six lanes of traffic.

_____ 10. Machines can complete some tasks more quickly and accurately than human beings can.

Word Skills

Name _____ Date _____

True-False

Decide whether each statement is true or false. Write *T* for True or *F* for False. Use the glossary for help if needed.

_____ **1.** Imaginary creatures called unicorns do not actually *exist*.

_____ **2.** If you knew the chemical would *corrode* metal, you would use it to protect the finish of a new car.

_____ **3.** A person with great *refinement* has crude habits and unpolished manners.

_____ **4.** A good manager tries to hire *efficient* workers.

_____ **5.** People who study the *economy* pay careful attention to the production, selling, and buying of goods and services.

_____ **6.** Someone who does not like *isolation* would enjoy staying alone in a cabin in the woods.

_____ **7.** A *systematic* person would probably arrange his or her books in an organized way.

_____ **8.** Two people who wanted to avoid *contention* would probably argue loudly rather than talk about a topic quietly.

_____ **9.** A manager who approved a project would tell her staff to *proceed*.

_____ **10.** If the woman wanted a job, she would probably *apply* by sending in a resume.

Suffix Additions

The vocabulary words below are from the selection. Write the matching related word on the lines before each suffix. Note that some words have spelling changes when a suffix is added. Use a dictionary for help if you need to.

1. artery: ___ ___ ___ ___ ___ ___ al

2. consume: ___ ___ ___ ___ ___ ___ er

3. contend: ___ ___ ___ ___ ___ ___ ___ ion

4. corrosion: ___ ___ ___ ___ ___ ___ ive

5. isolate: ___ ___ ___ ___ ___ ___ ion

The Latin Root *jacere*

The word *injection* comes from the Latin root *jacere*, meaning "to throw." The following words also come from this root:

dejected	**eject**	**inject**	**project**	**reject**

Match each word on the left with its definition on the right. Write the appropriate letter on each line.

_____ **1.** inject   **A** force out

_____ **2.** dejected   **B** refuse

_____ **3.** eject   **C** forecast

_____ **4.** project   **D** insert

_____ **5.** reject   **E** miserable

Sentence Completion

Use the words that come from the root *jacere* to complete these sentences.

1. The veterinarian decided to _____ a painkiller into the dog's cut paw to relieve the discomfort.

2. When a product does not meet required standards, an inspector is supposed to

_____ it.

3. The _____ team left the court slowly after losing the painfully close contest.

4. The newscasters all _____ rain next week, but I'm hoping for snow.

5. The speaker asked the police to _____ the troublemakers from the demonstration.

Name _____ Date _____

Writing

Imagine that you are looking for a summer job. You find this want ad:

> **Wanted:** Responsible student to care for our house while we are on vacation. Duties include lawn and garden care, watering houseplants, and feeding our cat and fish. Apply by letter, stating your qualifications, to Summer Job, Box 99, Austin, TX 78759.

Write an application letter for this job, describing your qualifications.

- Tell what your qualifications are. Have you looked after a house or an animal before?
- Tell what character traits you have that would make you suited to this job. For example, are you organized? Are you responsible?

Be sure to use some of the vocabulary words from this unit in your writing.

_____

_____

_____

_____

_____

_____

_____

_____

_____

_____

_____

_____

Writing

Vocabulary in Context G8, SV 9780547625812

Underground Palace

Read the selection. Think about the meanings of the **boldfaced** words. Then go back to the selection. Underline the words or sentences that give you a clue to the meaning of each **boldfaced** word.

As daylight was beginning to fade one summer day in 1901 in New Mexico, a young cowboy observed something strange in the familiar **landscape**. The cowboy, Jim White, thought he knew just about every rock and shrub of the countryside around him. Yet he didn't remember seeing anything like this before. It looked like a black cloud was emerging from a hole in the ground. White rode closer for a better look. It was then that he recognized the wispy dark shape as a flock of bats—thousands of them—escaping from the hole.

White peered into the mysterious thirty-foot shaft and decided to get some tools. He returned the next day with rope, wire, and an ax. Constructing a rope ladder, he descended into the darkness. When he reached the floor, he lit his lantern and found himself in a large open area that he soon realized was the entrance to a cave.

Jim White had never explored a cave before and was astonished by the unusual **features** he saw. A series of tunnels **radiated** from the entrance. The tunnels all started from the same open area, but then they branched out in all directions. Some of the tunnels had **alcoves**, little nooks that looked like small rooms. There were long, thin, jagged formations, called **stalactites**, growing down from the ceiling. Similar formations, called **stalagmites**, were growing up from the floor of the cave.

White was amazed at the immense size of the cavern, its eerie silence, and the dazzling **iridescent** colors that changed as he shifted his lantern from wall to wall. It was difficult for him to believe that this splendid underground palace was **unspoiled**, completely untouched by human beings. He was eager to tell his friends about the **magnificence** and grandeur he had observed.

To his surprise, his friends found his description unbelievable. But as other people explored the cave after him, the world recognized that this cowboy had made a significant contribution to **speleology**, the study of caves. Today, Jim White's discovery is known as Carlsbad Caverns, one of the world's most magnificent cave systems. It became a national park in 1930 and is visited each year by thousands of tourists.

Vocabulary in Context G8, SV 9780547625812

Context Clues

Meanings for the vocabulary words are given below. Go back to the selection and read each sentence that contains a vocabulary word. If you still cannot tell the meaning, look for clues in the sentences that come before and after the one with the vocabulary word. Write each word from the box beside its meaning.

alcoves	unspoiled	stalactites	stalagmites	iridescent
speleology	landscape	magnificence	features	radiated

1. _____ : limestone formations that hang from the ceilings of caves

2. _____ : limestone deposits, resembling icicles, that rise from cave floors

3. _____ : spread out from a center in all directions

4. _____ : splendor; beauty

5. _____ : a stretch of natural scenery

6. _____ : not touched or marred; undamaged

7. _____ : showing many colors that constantly change in the light

8. _____ : nooks; small recessed sections of rooms

9. _____ : the study and exploration of caves and their contents

10. _____ : characteristics; special parts

Vocabulary in Context

Cloze Paragraphs

Use the words from the box to complete the passage. Use context clues to help you. Then reread the passage to be sure it makes sense.

alcove	radiated	landscape	magnificence	iridescent
speleology	stalagmites	stalactites	unspoiled	features

My older sister is a cave explorer, and she calls (1) _____ the most fascinating study in the world. Not long ago, she invited me to go along on one of her cave explorations. I was hesitant at first because I am afraid of bats, but she assured me that the bats would probably be more afraid of me and would head for some tiny (2) _____, or nook, to hide in until we passed by. So, with that assurance, off we went.

As we drove toward the cave, I was surprised by the (3) _____ around us. I had expected a very hilly mountainous region to be the home of a grand cave, but this area seemed to just have patches of rolling hills. My sister explained that one of the (4) _____ of this area was a large amount of limestone in the soil. She said that when I was inside the cave, I would understand the significance of this characteristic.

Once inside, I immediately understood what she had meant. Hanging from the roof of the cave were huge limestone icicles, which my sister called (5) _____. Similar-looking limestone creations were rising up from the floor. These my sister called (6) _____. Then she cautioned me to stay beside her and not to wander off alone into a tunnel. So many of them (7) _____ from this central room that she would never have known how to find me.

As we walked through the cave, my sister told me its history. It was discovered by people who were searching for opals. These lovely (8) _____ stones, which change colors in the light, are quite valuable. There are no opals to be found around here, but at least one good thing came of the explorers' efforts—the discovery of this cave.

As I stood in the cave, awed by the splendor, awed by the (9) _____ of this natural place, I finally understood why my sister is a speleologist. In a world where people seem to touch and often mar things, how wonderful it is to find something completely (10) _____!

Vocabulary in Context

Name _____   Date _____

Word Groups

As you read each pair of words, think about how they are alike. Write the word from the box that best completes each group.

| alcove | iridescent | magnificence |
| landscape | unspoiled | features |

1. aspects, characteristics, _____

2. beauty, grandeur, _____

3. niche, nook, _____

4. scene, environment, _____

5. brilliant, shimmering, _____

6. untouched, undamaged, _____

Challenge Yourself

1. Name two features that distinguish birds from fish.

   _____

2. Name two things you might see in a desert landscape.

   _____

3. Name two adjectives you might use to describe the magnificence of a sunset.

   _____

Vocabulary in Context G8, SV 9780547625812

Vocabulary in Context

Word Pairs

Words with similar parts may have related meanings. Study each word pair. Think about how the meanings of the words are alike. Then write a sentence for each word.

1. radiate—radiated

_____

_____

2. spoil—unspoiled

_____

_____

3. speleology—speleologist

_____

_____

4. magnificent—magnificence

_____

_____

Forming Words

Using the letters found in the word *magnificence*, make as many words as you can of four or more letters. Form at least ten words. For example, the word *mince* can be formed using the letters in *magnificence*.

1. _____   6. _____

2. _____   7. _____

3. _____   8. _____

4. _____   9. _____

5. _____   10. _____

Standardized Test Practice

Circle the letter of the word or words that best complete the sentence.

TIP
Read carefully. Use the other words in the sentence to help you choose the correct word.

1. A *landscape* is made up of
   A caves.   C natural scenery.
   B paintings.   D ocean waves.

2. *Alcoves* are like small
   A towns.   C coves.
   B alleys.   D rooms.

3. *Radiated* means spread out from the
   A back.   C front.
   B center.   D space.

4. The *features* of something are its characteristics, or
   A qualities.   C items.
   B quantities.   D symbols.

5. *Stalactites* are found on a cave's
   A floor.   C entrance.
   B ceiling.   D outside.

6. *Stalagmites* are found on a cave's
   A floor.   C roof.
   B ceiling.   D outside.

7. *Speleology* is a prime interest of a
   A spy.   C mountain climber.
   B sailor.   D cave explorer.

8. The word *iridescent* might be used to describe a
   A person.   C scent.
   B soap bubble.   D hill.

9. Something that is *unspoiled* has not been
   A sold.   C radiated.
   B cooked.   D damaged.

10. Something having *magnificence* has
    A identity.   C splendor.
    B ugliness.   D insignificance.

Vocabulary in Context

Name _____ Date _____

Understanding Related Words

The following words can be related to the topic of exploration. See how many of the words you already know. Use the glossary to find the definitions of unfamiliar words.

analyze	ascertain	controversial	cosmos	immensity
inevitable	infinite	inquiry	invaluable	probe

Write the word from the box next to its definition. Check your answers in a dictionary or in the glossary.

1. _____ : to study carefully

2. _____ : great size

3. _____ : the universe, all of space

4. _____ : to explore

5. _____ : certain to happen

6. _____ : endless

7. _____ : causing questions and arguments

8. _____ : research; investigation

9. _____ : priceless

10. _____ : to find out

Name Game

1. Name two things that are inevitable in your daily life.

_____

2. Name two animals known for their immensity.

_____

3. Name two things you consider to be invaluable.

_____

4. Name two things about the future you would like to ascertain.

_____

Vocabulary in Context G8, SV 9780547625812

Word Skills

Dictionary Skills

The pronunciation key in a dictionary explains how a word is said aloud. Study the pronunciation key below. Then look at the five words and their pronunciation. Answer each question by writing the correct word or words.

a at	**i** it	**u** up	**a** in about
ā ape	**ī** ice	**o͞o** food	**e** in taken
e end	**o** hot	**ch** chin	ə ⎰ **i** in pencil
ē me	**ō** old		**o** in lemon
			u in circus

immensity (i men´si tē)   **cosmos** (koz´məs, koz´mōs)
probe (prōb)   **inevitable** (in ev´i tə bəl)
infinite (in´fə nit)

1. Which word has the same *o* sound as in *go*? _____

2. Which word has the same *o* sound as in *hot*? _____

3. Which word has the *k* sound of *c*? _____

4. Which three words have the same *i* sound as in *it*? _____

_____   _____

Rewriting Sentences

Rewrite each sentence using one of the words from the box.

controversial	analyze	invaluable	ascertain

1. My brother's help on this project was extremely valuable.

_____

2. Once we have all of the information, we will study it very carefully.

_____

3. The team's decision to elect a captain was argued about endlessly.

_____

4. We need to find out how many people are coming to dinner.

_____

Word Skills

Synonyms

Write the letter of the word that is the synonym of the capitalized word.

_____ 1. ANALYZE

    A defeat   **B** shrink   **C** exhaust   **D** study

_____ 2. CONTROVERSIAL

    A invaluable   **B** disputed   **C** mysterious   **D** forbidden

_____ 3. COSMOS

    A foreground   **B** universe   **C** planet   **D** sun

_____ 4. INFINITE

    A accurate   **B** important   **C** endless   **D** inevitable

_____ 5. INVALUABLE

    A priceless   **B** diminishing   **C** confusing   **D** fascinating

_____ 6. IMMENSITY

    A appetite   **B** cosmos   **C** ascent   **D** hugeness

_____ 7. INQUIRY

    A test   **B** search   **C** riddle   **D** solution

_____ 8. ASCERTAIN

    A find out   **B** write in   **C** make up   **D** ignore

_____ 9. PROBE

    A destroy   **B** improve   **C** ascertain   **D** explore

_____ 10. INEVITABLE

    A impossible   **B** certain   **C** infinite   **D** amusing

Name _____   Date _____

Writing

Carlsbad Caverns is a very large system of underground caverns. Think about a natural wonder that you have seen or would like to see. Tell about it in a paragraph.

- Tell where this particular natural wonder is located.
- Describe it using vivid adjectives.
- Explain why you find it interesting.

Use some vocabulary words from this unit in your writing.

_____

_____

_____

_____

_____

_____

_____

_____

_____

_____

_____

_____

_____

Writing

Vocabulary in Context G8, SV 9780547625812

Tragedy and Triumph

Read the selection. Think about the meanings of the **boldfaced** words. Then go back to the selection. Underline the words or sentences that give you a clue to the meaning of each **boldfaced** word.

Four-year-old Christopher Pylant was a very sick little boy. He suffered from a terrible **affliction** that made him **paralytic**, unable to move his body. His doctors in Georgia said he had a brain tumor, a frightening condition that is often incurable. Despite this **diagnosis**, Christopher's parents refused to give up hope. They traveled to Baltimore, Maryland, to consult with the celebrated physician Dr. Benjamin Carson.

Dr. Carson's specialty was **neurology**, the branch of medicine dealing with the nervous system and its diseases. He had become the chief of neurology at Johns Hopkins School of Medicine in Baltimore in 1984, when he was only thirty-three. He was also a **pediatrician**, specializing in the care of children. If this man couldn't help their son, the Pylants knew they had no hope.

Dr. Carson was highly qualified in children's medicine. He had performed many difficult operations on the brain. He even separated baby twins who had been born joined at the head. But in Christopher's case, he knew there was little reason to be **optimistic**, or hopeful, that an operation would be successful. After studying the X-rays, he could provide Christopher's parents with little **consolation**. The X-rays showed that the tumor had already extended into the many deep crevices in the brain. The tumor appeared to have consumed the brain stem. This is the part of the brain located at the top of the spine, through which all nerve impulses flow. Dr. Carson came to the sad conclusion that his years of **clinical** experience, treating actual patients, were of no use in this case.

The Pylants, however, would not give up hope. They urged Dr. Carson to operate to remove the tumor. He finally agreed, and the **surgical** team prepared to perform surgery on Christopher. After two long operations, Dr. Carson accomplished what he at first thought was impossible. He completely removed all of the cancerous tumors and exposed a healthy brain stem. After being **hospitalized** only one month, Christopher Pylant returned home. Now, Christopher is a healthy young adult. Thanks to two loving parents and a dedicated doctor, Christopher Pylant grew into a future no one thought he had.

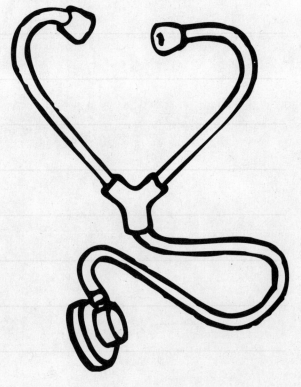

Name _____ Date _____

Context Clues

Read each pair of sentences. Look for context clues to help you complete the sentences with a word or words from the box.

affliction	diagnosis	paralytic	optimistic	pediatrician
hospitalized	consolation	neurology	surgical	clinical

1. When people are very ill, they need treatment that they cannot receive at home. They are

   _____ so that doctors and nurses can care for them.

2. A doctor who has experience in treating patients will examine each sick person. The doctor uses

   that _____ experience to make a judgment about the patient's illness.

3. The doctor will look for symptoms to help pinpoint the problem. Once the doctor makes a

   _____, treatment begins.

4. A doctor may have several options to choose from. In a serious case, the doctor may need to operate,

   so a _____ procedure is planned.

5. Instead, a doctor may have hope that an operation is not needed. The doctor is

   _____ that drugs can cure the problem.

6. Sadly, sometimes a disease is so serious that nothing can be done to help a patient. When

   a person has such an _____, a doctor can offer only comfort, or

   _____.

7. Occasionally, a doctor may believe there is no hope, only to be surprised by the patient. This may

   happen with a _____ patient, where it is seems unlikely that the patient
   will be able to move a limb again—yet the person does!

8. Some kinds of doctors deal with more life-threatening illnesses than others. Doctors in the field of

   _____, which has to do with the brain, are faced with many crucial decisions.

9. Others, like those who care for children, may see a range of illnesses. A _____
   may treat anything from a cold to a broken leg.

Name _____ Date _____

Medical Words

The words in the box all have to do with the science of medicine. Write each word beside its meaning.

diagnosis	paralytic	pediatrician	hospitalized
surgical	clinical	neurology	

1. placed in a hospital for treatment _____

2. the branch of medicine devoted to the brain and nervous system _____

3. having to do with the direct observation and treatment of sick people _____

4. a doctor who specializes in treating babies and children _____

5. having to do with the removal or repair of stricken body parts _____

6. a condition in which one is unable to move _____

7. conclusion reached after a doctor studies symptoms _____

Writing Sentences

Write an original sentence with each of the words in the box.

affliction	neurology	consolation
clinical	optimistic	pediatrician

1. _____

2. _____

3. _____

4. _____

5. _____

6. _____

Word Map

Use the words in the box to complete the word map about doctors. Add other words that you know to each group.

| diagnosis | afflictions | paralytic | surgical | optimistic | pediatrician |

Vocabulary in Context

Kinds of Doctors

1. _____
2. _____
3. _____
4. _____
5. _____

What a Doctor Needs to Be

1. _____
2. _____
3. _____
4. _____
5. _____

DOCTORS

Problems or Conditions They Treat

1. _____
2. _____
3. _____
4. _____
5. _____

What Doctors Do

1. _____
2. _____
3. _____
4. _____
5. _____

Name _____ Date _____

Synonyms and Antonyms

Synonyms are words that have similar meanings, while antonyms are words that have opposite meanings. Look at the words below. If they are synonyms, put a (✓) in the Synonyms column. If they are antonyms, put a (✓) in the Antonyms column.

	Antonyms	**Synonyms**
1. affliction—disease	_____	_____
2. optimistic—pessimistic	_____	_____
3. consolation—comfort	_____	_____
4. clinical—medical	_____	_____
5. misdiagnosis—diagnosis	_____	_____

The Suffixes -ician and -ist

The suffixes –ician and –ist refer to someone who does something. A *pediatrician* is a doctor who cares for children. A *neurologist* is a doctor who works on the nervous system.

Add the correct suffix to these words to make a noun that means "someone who does something." (Note: Sometimes you will have to drop or change letters before you add the suffix. If you need to, use a dictionary to check your spelling.)

1. beauty: _____

2. biology: _____

3. statistics: _____

4. art: _____

5. type: _____

6. music: _____

7. chemical: _____

8. speleology: _____

Standardized Test Practice

Circle the letter of the word or words that best take the place of the italicized word.

TIP Think about the meaning of the italicized words before you choose an answer. Don't be fooled by a word that looks similar to an italicized word.

1. The game-show host offered *consolation* to the contestants. His words made them feel better, even though they lost.

   A money   C affliction
   B television   D comfort

2. Before the test, John felt *optimistic*. He was sure his chances of passing were good.

   A hopeful   C oppressive
   B worried   D paralytic

3. The dog had a strange *affliction*. It was sick for weeks.

   A flea   C consolation
   B disease   D look

4. Sometimes the cat seemed *paralytic*. Other times, it was able to get around just fine.

   A optimistic   C active
   B unable to move D unable to participate

5. The patient was prepared for the *surgical* procedure. Doctors wheeled her toward the operating room.

   A experimental   C in and out
   B secret   D removal or repair

6. The surgeon made a *clinical* study of the disease. He had treated many patients with this same problem.

   A client   C in the hospital
   B shallow   D in the home

7. After the operation, Jeri was *hospitalized* for several days. Then she went home.

   A treated in a hotel   C cared for by parents
   B held by hostages   D treated in a hospital

8. A doctor of *neurology* examined me. He said I am healthy.

   A new illnesses   C the skeletal system
   B children   D the nervous system

9. The doctor's *diagnosis* was an optimistic one. She said the patient would be well soon.

   A neurology   C speech
   B dispatch   D conclusion

10. Marsha wants to be a *pediatrician*. She hopes to cure sick young people.

   A children's doctor   C artist
   B police officer   D pedicurist

Vocabulary in Context

Understanding Related Words

The words in the box can be related to science and technology. In this case, the words are related to Charles Richter's invention of the Richter scale, which measures the shock waves from an earthquake. See how many of the words you already know. Use the glossary to find the definitions of unfamiliar words.

accuracy	anticipate	avert	compute	contributor
devastate	evaluate	inadequate	lethal	seismic

Read each pair of sentences. Look for clues to help you complete one of the sentences with a word from the box. Write the word on the line.

1. History is filled with stories of earthquakes. Until recently, however, people had _____, or not enough, information about what caused them.

2. In 1755, an earthquake of _____ force struck the city of Lisbon, Portugal. Thousands of people died.

3. The heart of the city was destroyed. The citizens saw firsthand how an earthquake could _____ an area.

4. A man named John Mitchell made some studies after the Lisbon earthquake. In sharing what he learned, Mitchell became an early _____ to our knowledge of earthquakes.

5. Mitchell discovered that _____ waves, the waves from an earthquake, disturb everything in their path. This is why extremely large waves form in the ocean.

6. At first, people could judge how serious an earthquake had been only by comparing it to other earthquakes. To do this, they would _____ the destruction caused by each quake.

7. Looking at the wreckage left by an earthquake was not a precise way to measure its strength. A method whose _____ could not be questioned was needed.

8. Charles Richter knew that using mathematics would help people to measure accurately. He created a scale that scientists can use to _____ a number that tells how severe a quake is.

9. Increased knowledge of earthquakes has helped scientists learn how to predict when and where an earthquake may strike. Being able to _____ a quake has saved many lives.

10. People who live in earthquake areas have also learned how to prevent some kinds of damage from occurring. They have learned to _____ a disaster by building stronger homes.

Word Skills

Name _____ Date _____

Word Groups

As you read each pair of words, think about how they are alike. Write the word from the box that best completes each group.

| compute | evaluate | lethal | devastate | contributor | anticipate |

1. deadly, fatal, _____

2. ruin, destroy, _____

3. foresee, expect, _____

4. add, figure, _____

5. assistant, partner, _____

6. judge, assess, _____

Dictionary Skills

Each numbered item has two parts. Answer the first part by writing a word from the box.
Answer the second part by circling the correct choice. Use the pronunciation key in a dictionary
to help you when necessary.

| accuracy | inadequate | avert | contributor | anticipate |

1. Write the correct spelling of in ad´i kwit. _____
   It means **A** more than is required. **B** less than is required.

2. Write the correct spelling of an tis´ə pāt´. _____
   It means **A** to see in advance. **B** to be surprised.

3. Write the correct spelling of kən trib´yə tər. _____
   It means **A** one who adds something. **B** one who takes away.

4. Write the correct spelling of ak´yər ə sē. _____
   It means **A** sloppiness. **B** correctness.

5. Write the correct spelling of ə vûrt´. _____
   It means **A** to hide from. **B** to prevent.

Word Skills

Name _____ Date _____

Word Game

The underlined letters in each sentence below are part of one of the words in the box. Use the underlined letters and the context of the sentence to determine the correct word. Write the word on the line.

evaluate	contributor	seismic	averted	devastate
inadequate	accuracy	anticipate	compute	lethal

1. The store placed an <u>ad</u> in the newspaper, but it wasn't enough to bring in new customers.

   _____

2. The cats sit by Meg's chair and look forward to a <u>pat</u> on the head. _____

3. That doctor has treated many athletes and has added to medical knowledge about how to treat a

   broken <u>rib</u>. _____

4. The hurricane could destroy all the crops in the <u>state</u>, which would ruin many farms and raise the

   prices of fruits and vegetables. _____

5. These chemicals and soaps could cause the death of a child, so please <u>let</u> me move them to a safer

   place. _____

6. I can believe <u>Cy</u> because his descriptions are almost always correct. _____

7. I think it is the shock waves that follow an <u>ea</u>rthquake that are the most frightening.

   _____

8. We <u>ate</u> dinner at a new restaurant, and after we thought about it, we decided it was one of the best

   meals we had ever eaten. _____

9. We have been studying the <u>Ute</u>, a tribe that lived in Utah, but we have not yet found out if they had a

   system for counting objects. _____

10. <u>Te</u>d turned his eyes away from the mess his baby brother had created on the kitchen floor.

    _____

Vocabulary in Context G8, SV 9780547625812

Writing

Advances in medicine have made it possible for children like Christopher Pylant to survive a brain tumor. Advances in science have made it possible for people to predict and prepare for earthquakes.

Write a letter describing an advance in the world of science that you believe has helped many people. It might be a new invention, like the computer, or an older discovery, like penicillin.

• Describe the scientific advance. Is it an invention? A new medicine? A new medical procedure?
• Tell which people are helped by it.
• Explain why you chose to write about it.

Use some vocabulary words from this unit in your writing.

_____

_____

_____

_____

_____

_____

_____

_____

_____

_____

_____

_____

_____

_____

_____

_____

_____

_____

Writing

Thomas Edison: The Early Years of Genius

by Howard Peet

Read the selection. Think about the meanings of the **boldfaced** words. Then go back to the selection. Underline the words or sentences that give you a clue to the meaning of each **boldfaced** word.

Most people in the United States have heard of Thomas Edison, but many people have never heard of his early struggles and disappointments. The author tells about Edison's youth and first efforts as an inventor.

Perhaps no other person has had a greater effect on modern life than Thomas Alva Edison (1847–1931), whose inventions include the electric light bulb, the phonograph, and the movie projector. In his lifetime he **acquired** 1,093 patents for his inventions. The vast number of his **achievements** brought him **universal** fame and made his name a household word. But such success was not easily won.

As a boy, Edison showed a tireless curiosity. His experience in public school was not a happy one, however. When he became **eligible** to attend school at the age of seven, his endless questions annoyed his teacher. The frustrated, impatient teacher even told Edison's mother that her son was retarded. Outraged at the teacher's negative **outlook**, the mother pulled her son out of school after only three months of formal education. Luckily, she was a gifted teacher herself, and she took responsibility for his learning. Soon he began to learn so fast that his mother could not keep up with him. Through wide reading and his own experiments, young Edison was discovering the excitement of modern science.

His family's **financial** difficulties forced Edison to take his first job at the age of twelve. He sold newspapers on a railway and used his spare time to conduct chemical experiments. Due to a **defect** in one of his experiments, a fire accidentally started in the baggage car. As punishment, the conductor boxed his ears and threw him and his chemicals off the train. The conductor's slaps may have contributed to the development of Edison's deafness, which became almost total in his later years.

Edison continued work in **pedestrian** jobs during his adolescent years. Though the jobs did not match his ability or potential, he put his free time to good use by continuing his self-education. Eventually, he traveled around the country while working as a **vagabond** telegrapher; the little money he made was spent mostly on equipment or books for his experiments.

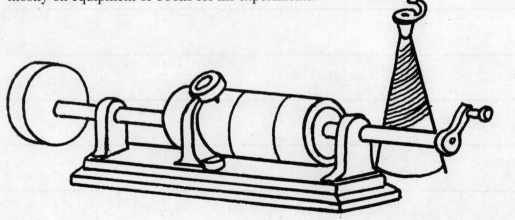

phonograph

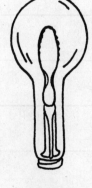

light bulb

While in his early twenties, Edison was awarded his first patent. He designed a voting machine to be used by an **exclusive** group—the United States Congress. Members of Congress could sit with this machine at their seats and push a yes or a no button. Each member's vote would immediately be **duplicated** on a large board at the front of the congressional chamber. Edison went to Washington, D.C., to convince Congress to purchase his machine. The representatives treated him as a **prominent** person, allowing him to speak before a committee.

However, the invention was turned down because it recorded results too quickly. The members of Congress wanted to preserve the forty-five minutes it took to record a roll call vote. This gave them time to trade votes or prepare for any possible **veto** by the president. Following his rejection, Edison said, "I will never again invent anything nobody wants." He set one **requirement** for all his future inventions; they must meet "the **desperate** needs of the world."

Edison's determination did not **falter**. Even though he was so poor that he had to sleep in the office where he worked, he continued to explore ways of inventing or improving machines. While working for a company in New York City, he studied the operation of the ticker, a telegraphic device used to record changes in the stock market prices. One day the ticker broke down, and none of the repair people could fix it. To the amazement of the office manager, Edison fixed the machine himself. He was then given the job of supervising the **maintenance** of the ticker. With his **typical** experimental approach, he proceeded to find ways of making the machine more reliable and efficient.

Edison received several patents for his improvement of the stock ticker. The president of the company that employed him bought the rights to these patents for $40,000, an enormous sum at that time. Edison turned around and invested his money in a laboratory workshop, where he could pursue his research around the clock.

For more than fifty years Edison continued to explore the mysteries of science and machines. This work that he loved **monopolized** his life to the point that he rarely got more than four hours of sleep a night. He **relished** his investigations so much that he had little time left for family or friends. Yet what he accomplished eventually changed the way ordinary people lived their lives. No inventor ever gave more to the world.

Vocabulary in Context G8, SV 9780547625812

Context Clues

Write the letter of the word or phrase that is closest in meaning to the word or words in italics. Use context clues to help you choose the correct answer.

Vocabulary in Context

_____ 1. Alicia regarded learning to swim as a major *achievement*, the most important thing she had done all summer.

    A problem   **B** failure   **C** accomplishment   **D** skill

_____ 2. It takes years of schooling and training to *acquire* the skills needed to become a good doctor.

    A obtain   **B** find   **C** lose   **D** desire

_____ 3. The only *defect* in David's golf swing was a slight bend of his left arm, which decreased his accuracy.

    A strength   **B** fault   **C** habit   **D** virtue

_____ 4. As she hung from the airplane's wing, the stuntwoman feared she was in a *desperate* situation.

    A urgent   **B** strange   **C** athletic   **D** graceful

_____ 5. Ted was able to *duplicate* the old drawing, matching the original in every detail.

    A read over   **B** copy   **C** change   **D** print

_____ 6. The law sets a minimum age for candidates to be president of the United States. To be *eligible*, you must be at least thirty-five years old.

    A interested   **B** intelligent enough   **C** qualified   **D** famous

_____ 7. The club was very *exclusive*; only those students who spoke a foreign language could join.

    A large   **B** selective   **C** exciting   **D** expensive

_____ 8. After her illness, Carla was so weak that she *faltered* and fell against the stair rail.

    A jumped up   **B** ran over   **C** yelled   **D** stumbled

_____ 9. After her son received a large sum of money from his grandparents, Mrs. Cano gave him *financial* advice.

    A employment   **B** final   **C** money-related   **D** health-related

_____ 10. The *maintenance* of the Cleasons' car involved replacing the filters and changing the spark plugs.

    A driving   **B** upkeep   **C** sale   **D** licensing

_____ 11. Jesse loved to talk so much that he *monopolized* many conversations.

    A recorded   **B** ignored   **C** took turns in   **D** controlled

12. _____ Gail's *outlook on* life is positive. She believes she can accomplish anything she puts her mind to.

    A view of   **B** criticism of   **C** study of   **D** writing about

13. _____ The use of *pedestrian* language can make a composition seem lifeless. Interesting writing requires fresh and original language.

    A fascinating   **B** unusual   **C** dull   **D** thoughtful

14. _____ The clown's most *prominent* feature was his electrified red nose.

    A handsome   **B** plain   **C** outstanding   **D** neglected

15. _____ Tom spent many hours reading biographies and adventure stories at the library; he obviously *relished* reading.

    A enjoyed   **B** dreaded   **C** disliked   **D** regretted

16. _____ A passing grade on the unit test is the main *requirement* for going on to the next unit of the book.

    A problem   **B** condition   **C** examination   **D** excuse

17. _____ Sandy beaches and palm trees are a *typical* sight on the Florida coastline. Each year thousands of tourists come to enjoy them.

    A rare   **B** forgettable   **C** normal   **D** believable

18. _____ Love and encouragement are *universal* needs, necessary for the healthy development of every child in every culture and country.

    A limited   **B** timely   **C** foreign   **D** worldwide

19. _____ In the Middle Ages, *vagabond* minstrels would make their way from town to town, singing songs and telling stories.

    A criminal   **B** wandering   **C** ignorant   **D** silly

20. _____ The president's *veto* of a bill may prevent it from becoming law. A veto can be overturned only if two-thirds of each House of Congress votes in favor of the bill.

    A rejection   **B** misunderstanding   **C** approval   **D** description

Vocabulary in Context

Understanding Multiple-Meaning Words

Each box in this exercise contains a **boldfaced** word with its definitions. Read the definitions and then the sentences that use the word. Write the letter of the definition that applies to each sentence.

> **pedestrian**
> a. a person who is walking (noun)
> b. unimaginative; dull (adjective)
> c. of or for people who are walking (adjective)

_____ 1. The *pedestrian* bridge was crowded with sightseers and shoppers.

_____ 2. In contrast to Bill's *pedestrian* answer, Christine's solution was original.

_____ 3. Cars must yield the right of way to a *pedestrian*.

> **defect**
> a. a fault or imperfection (noun)
> b. desert one's country; abandon a cause or group, often to support another (verb)

_____ 4. The foreign visitor went to the embassy and said he wanted to *defect* to the United States.

_____ 5. The only *defect* in Bob's plan was that he could not get his car started.

_____ 6. The new choir director was so strict that several singers wanted to *defect* to the glee club.

> **relish**
> a. a distinctive or appetizing flavor (noun)
> b. great enjoyment or pleasure (noun)
> c. a food such as pickles or olives (noun)
> d. to enjoy; to like (verb)

_____ 7. Larry asked Betty to bring *relishes* to the barbeque.

_____ 8. People who *relish* their jobs usually do them well.

_____ 9. Mr. Oliver listened with *relish* as his piano students performed their recital.

_____ 10. There was a *relish* of garlic in the spaghetti sauce.

Standardized Test Practice

Circle the letter of the word that is closest in meaning to the capitalized word.

> **TIP**
>
> Remember that you are looking for a synonym, a word that has the same or almost the same meaning as the capitalized word.

1. VAGABOND

A stealing   C residing

B working   D wandering

2. DUPLICATE

A copy   C create

B present   D control

3. ELIGIBLE

A handsome   C expensive

B qualified   D improper

4. FALTER

A corrode   C stumble

B pursue   D destroy

5. FINANCIAL

A monetary   C needy

B considerable   D wealthy

6. OUTLOOK

A destiny   C honesty

B viewpoint   D quality

7. REQUIREMENT

A rule   C choice

B reluctance   D obstacle

8. UNIVERSAL

A everywhere   C instinctive

B large   D national

Circle the letter of the word that is most nearly *opposite* in meaning to the capitalized word.

9. DESPERATE

A optimistic   C annoyed

B tired   D popular

10. EXCLUSIVE

A common   C shy

B understandable   D silent

11. MAINTENANCE

A repair   C purity

B procedure   D destruction

12. MONOPOLIZE

A control   C simplify

B share   D dislodge

13. PROMINENT

A false   C superior

B inconsiderate   D unnoticeable

14. ACHIEVEMENT

A sorrow   C failure

B act   D thrill

Understanding Related Words

The words in the box are closely related to the vocabulary words. See how many of the words you already know. Use the glossary to find the definitions of unfamiliar words.

achieve	acquisition	atypical	defective	despair
desperation	duplication	eligibility	exclude	finance
financier	include	ineligible	inquire	maintain
monopoly	prominence	require	typify	universe

Write the word from the box that best completes the meaning of the sentence.

1. Many schools _____ that new students have physical exams before they start classes.

2. Jim wrote to _____ when we would be going to Seattle to visit him.

3. Until the breakup of AT&T, the company had a(an) _____ on telephone service in the United States.

4. The toaster Pun bought was _____, so she had to exchange it for one that worked.

5. The art collector paid a great deal of money for the _____ of a famous painting.

6. Before their rise to _____, many famous actors held a variety of low-paying jobs and went through periods of unemployment.

7. Yolanda worked hard to _____ her goal of learning to swim before camp was over.

8. In order to get a job, her family insisted she must _____ a B average for the entire school year.

9. Because of a(an) _____ on the mailing list, Marty got two copies of the computer magazine he ordered.

10. Cacti, scrub trees, and sand _____ the scenery of much of the Southwest.

Word Groups

Each of the sentences below needs to be completed by a pair of words that are related in some way. Write the two related words from the box that best complete each sentence.

achieve	atypical	despair	eligibility	exclude	finance
achievement	typical	desperation	ineligible	include	financier

1. The honor society voted to _____ students who had B averages and

   _____ students whose averages were lower.

2. Bobby is a(an) _____ ten-year-old who has to be urged to practice the piano;

   however, his friend Janie is somewhat _____ because she loves to practice and

   never needs to be reminded.

3. Stocks, bonds, and other aspects of the world of _____ are often confusing to

   someone who is not a professional _____.

4. The athletic association, which rules on the _____ of high school basketball

   players, declared that players over twenty years old were _____.

5. Some of the stranded Scouts began to _____ of ever getting back to the

   campsite, but their leader wisely warned them that _____ and panic would

   only make their problems worse.

6. The students were thrilled to _____ a high grade on their drama project, a

   play they wrote and performed. However, they all agreed their greatest _____

   had been the review in the school newspaper, which called their performance funny and

   thought provoking.

Word Skills

Name _____   Date _____

The Latin Root *uni*

The Latin root *uni* means "one." This root is found in the word *universal*, as well as the related word *universe*. Other words, such as *unicycle*, *uniform*, *unit*, and *unite*, all contain this root.

Write the word from the box that best completes each sentence. Use a dictionary if needed.

unicycle	united	uniform	unit	universe

1. Whether in Maine or California, stoplights are _____ throughout the country—always red on top, yellow in the middle, and green on the bottom.

2. In order to ride a _____ without falling over, the rider must have a very good sense of balance.

3. In Mr. Cato's geography class, the _____ on Argentina lasted for one week.

4. Canada is a collection of ten provinces and three territories _____ into one country.

5. The Milky Way Galaxy is one of the many galaxies in our _____.

The Greek Root *mono*

The Greek root *mono* comes from the Greek word *monos*, which means "single" or "alone." The word *monopolized* and the related word *monopoly* contain this root. The root can also be found in the words listed below.

Write the word from the box that best completes each sentence. Use a dictionary if needed.

monarch	monoplane	monorail	monotone	monotony

1. King Olaf V, the _____ of Norway, reigned from 1957 to 1991.

2. Imagine the _____ of eating nothing but bread and water for a whole week!

3. A biplane has two wings; a_____ has one wing.

4. A train riding on a _____ carried visitors from downtown Seattle to the World's Fair in 1962.

5. Public speakers are urged not to talk in a _____ but to vary the pitch of their voice.

Writing

Write a short description of your outlook on life.

• Are you optimistic—that is, do you tend to take a hopeful view of things?

• Or are you pessimistic—do you tend to take a more gloomy view of things?

Tell whether you are generally optimistic or pessimistic. Include specific examples of things you have said or done that demonstrate your outlook. Be sure to use some of the vocabulary words from this unit in your writing.

_____

_____

_____

_____

_____

_____

_____

_____

_____

_____

_____

_____

_____

_____

_____

Food into Energy

Read the selection. Think about the meanings of the **boldfaced** words. Then go back to the selection. Underline the words or sentences that give you a clue to the meaning of each **boldfaced** word.

The human body is a kind of machine, and like any machine, it needs energy to do its work. The energy comes from the food you **consume**. After you chew and swallow food, it is broken down into small pieces and converted into the energy your body needs. This process is called **digestion**. The digestive system uses certain nourishing parts of food—called **nutrients**—for energy.

Most of the work of digesting food takes place in the stomach, where the food is mixed with various body fluids. These digestive fluids, or **enzymes**, break down the food into its basic chemicals, the same chemicals your body requires to stay physically fit. Some enzymes work only on **proteins**, nutrients made of nitrogen and found in meat, milk, eggs, and other foods. Other enzymes work only on **carbohydrates**, the sugars and starches found in such foods as candy, rice, and bread.

Digestion is completed in the small intestine, and the digested food enters your bloodstream through a process called **absorption**. The blood carries it to the muscles, bones, and other parts of the body. Your body uses the chemicals for energy to shoot a basketball or read this page. They also provide energy for your growth and for the repairing of cells. The amount of energy that the body needs varies from one individual to another. Children generally need more energy than adults, and larger people need more than smaller people.

The energy in food is measured in **calories**. A calorie is a unit used to measure the amount of energy supplied by foods. Most teenagers need about three thousand calories a day to stay healthy and active. When people do not eat sufficient quantities of nourishing foods, a **deficiency** of energy results. When this shortage becomes serious, the body suffers from **malnutrition**. Malnutrition can result from too little food or too much of the wrong kinds of food.

To stay healthy, a person should eat a balanced diet. That means eating foods from each of the food groups. It's not hard to do, and the reward is a body that is in top shape and full of energy!

Context Clues

Meanings for the vocabulary words are given below. Go back to the selection and read each sentence that contains a vocabulary word. If you still cannot tell the meaning, look for clues in the sentences that come before and after the one with the vocabulary word. Write each word before its meaning.

nutrients	proteins	absorption	malnutrition	consume
enzymes	deficiency	carbohydrates	calories	digestion

1. _____ : shortage; a lack of something required

2. _____ : eat or drink; use up

3. _____ : nutritious substances that are necessary for proper body functioning

4. _____ : the process by which the body breaks down food in the stomach to use as energy

5. _____ : chemical compounds such as starches and sugars

6. _____ : units used to measure the amount of energy supplied by various foods

7. _____ : a condition in which the body suffers from a lack of nutritious substances

8. _____ : chemical substances that help break down foods in the body

9. _____ : the process by which food enters the bloodstream after it has been broken down

10. _____ : chemical compounds that contain nitrogen and are found in meat, milk, and fish

Vocabulary in Context

Rewriting Sentences

Rewrite each sentence using one of the vocabulary words from the box.

malnutrition	enzymes	carbohydrates	consume

1. He follows a diet low in sugar and starches.

   _____

2. Chemical substances help your body digest food.

   _____

3. To lose weight, you must exercise more and eat less food.

   _____

4. The doctor found that the child suffered from a lack of nourishment.

   _____

Cloze Paragraphs

Use the words in the box to complete the passage. Then reread the passage to be sure it makes sense.

carbohydrates	nutrients	protein	absorption
digestion	consume	calories	deficiency

Are you eating the right foods, ones that provide all the (1) _____ your

body needs? Doctors recommend that teenagers (2) _____ about 3,000

(3) _____ a day. That may sound like you can eat a lot, but foods like potato chips

and doughnuts will quickly add up!

To avoid any kind of vitamin or mineral (4) _____, or shortage, you must eat a

balanced diet. This means eating plenty of fruits and vegetables, plus foods like pasta and rice, which are

high in (5) _____. You should also eat foods like chicken and fish, which are high

in (6) _____. An added bonus for eating the right kinds of foods is that they do not

cause problems in the stomach when it is time for (7) _____ to begin. Once they are

broken down, (8) _____ of the nutrients into the bloodstream takes place smoothly.

So eat right!

Tangled-Up Words

In the following passage, the underlined words do not make sense. But each sounds similar to a word in the box. Study the context in which the underlined words appear. For each word, find the word in the box that should be used in its place. Write the correct word on the numbered line.

nutrients	proteins	absorption	deficiency	consume
calories	malnutrition	carbohydrates	enzymes	digestion

Vocabulary in Context

In many ways, the human body is like a machine. You give it energy in the form of food, and it runs. But you can't feed it just any foods. It needs foods that contain the (1) nuclears that keep it running in top form.

There are many vitamins and minerals your body needs that you must make sure are contained in the foods you eat. Your body also needs certain (2) proceeds found in meat, milk, and fish. Your body depends on the (3) carpenters you (4) assume for high energy. Haven't you noticed that when you eat foods that contain sugar or starch, such as candy or potatoes, you have more get-up-and-go? But beware! Those same foods are also high in (5) canneries. To stay slim, you must eat them in moderation.

What happens to your body when you don't eat the right foods? The machine won't work right. One sign of problems may occur when (6) suggestion is taking place in your stomach. Very spicy or rich foods may be difficult for the (7) engines to break down and may make you feel uncomfortable. But even more serious problems will develop if you are not taking in enough vitamins and minerals. Then you may develop a (8) democracy.

The most serious condition occurs when your body is deprived of healthful foods for a long time. Then it can develop (9) malfunction. This means that when the process of (10) abbreviation takes place, very few healthful substances are taken into the bloodstream.

However, there is no need for these serious problems to occur. All your body needs to hum along like a well-tuned machine is a healthful diet. Give your body what it needs. You deserve it!

1. _____   6. _____

2. _____   7. _____

3. _____   8. _____

4. _____   9. _____

5. _____   10. _____

Name _____   Date _____

Word Game

Read each clue. Then write the word from the box that fits the clue. Use a dictionary or the glossary if you need help.

| enzymes | malnutrition | consume | calories | absorption | nutrients |

1. When you eat a sandwich, you do this. _____

2. Digested food enters the bloodstream through this process. _____

3. Without these, digestion would be impossible. _____

4. This is what the energy in food is measured in. _____

5. This is a result of not eating properly for a long time. _____

6. The nourishing parts of food are called this. _____

Challenge Yourself

1. Name two foods that are high in carbohydrates.

_____

_____

2. Name three sources of protein.

_____

_____

3. Name two causes of malnutrition.

_____

_____

_____

Vocabulary in Context G8, SV 9780547625812

Name _____   Date _____

Standardized Test Practice

Circle the letter of the word or words that best complete the sentence.

 TIP

> If you are not sure which word completes the sentence, do the best you can. Try to choose the answer that makes the most sense.

1. *Absorption* is the process through which food enters the

   A bloodstream.   **B** stomach.   **C** lungs.   **D** mouth.

2. The doctor thought the little girl was suffering from *malnutrition* because she had not

   A fished.   **B** cooked.   **C** eaten.   **D** run.

3. Calories measure

   A energy.   **B** fat.   **C** sugar.   **D** atoms.

4. To avoid a *deficiency* in your diet, it is important to eat

   A sweets like candy.   **C** a variety of healthful foods.

   B the same food every day.   **D** pizza and hot dogs.

5. The job of *enzymes* is to

   A break down food.   **C** store proteins.

   B fuel carbohydrates.   **D** prevent nutrition.

6. An example of a *carbohydrate* is

   A fish.   **B** bread.   **C** cheese.   **D** beef.

7. *Nutrients* are the nourishing parts of

   A intestines.   **B** food.   **C** enzymes.   **D** energy.

8. Another word for *consume* is

   A develop.   **B** assume.   **C** eat.   **D** add.

9. The process of *digestion* involves

   A making good dinners.   **C** choosing fresh vegetables.

   B eating three meals a day.   **D** breaking down food.

10. *Proteins* are found in all of these except

   A candy.   **B** meat.   **C** milk.   **D** fish.

Name _____ Date _____

Understanding Related Words

The words in the box relate to a different kind of energy—the kind that fuels our cars, machines, and lights. See how many of the following words you already know. Use the glossary to find the definitions of unfamiliar words.

commodity	compensate	complexity	conservationists	conversion
discretion	geothermal	replenished	statistics	wasteful

Meanings for the words in the box are given below. Write each word beside its meaning.

1. _____ : using or spending too much

2. _____ : the quality of being difficult to understand or complicated

3. _____ : filled again; furnished with a new supply

4. _____ : numbers that give facts about people, places, and things

5. _____ : anything bought and sold

6. _____ : produced by heat within the earth

7. _____ : make up for; make an equal payment for

8. _____ : freedom to act on one's own judgment; wise caution

9. _____ : the act of changing; turning from one thing into another

10. _____ : people who work to protect and save natural resources

Word Skills

Vocabulary in Context G8, SV 9780547625812

Analogies

An analogy shows the relationship between two pairs of words. Complete each of the following analogies by writing a word from the box on the line.

conservationists	geothermal	replenished	conversion	commodity

1. *Heat* is to *solar* as *steam* is to _____.

2. *Purchased* is to *restocked* as *consumed* is to _____.

3. *Choice* is to *selection* as *change* is to _____.

4. *Shopper* is to *consumer* as *product* is to _____.

5. *Revolution* is to *revolutionaries* as *conservation* is to _____.

Word Pairs

Words with similar parts may have related meanings. Study each word pair. Think about how the meanings of the words are alike. Check the meanings in the glossary. Then write a sentence for each word.

1. discreet—discretion

_____

_____

2. compensate—compensation

_____

_____

3. wasteful—wastefulness

_____

_____

4. statistics—statistical

_____

_____

5. complex—complexity

_____

_____

Word Skills

Word Play

The underlined letters in each sentence below are part of one of the words in the box. Use the underlined letters and the context of the sentence to determine the correct word. Write the word on the line.

commodity	compensate	complexity	conservationists	conversion
discretion	geothermal	replenished	statistics	wasteful

1. She reached for her **pen** so she could sign her employees' paychecks. _____

2. Concerned **as** she was about her grades, she continued to misuse her time and abilities.

   _____

3. When our neighbor returned all the tools he had borrowed, our once empty **shed** was again filled

   to capacity with equipment. _____

4. Don't try to **con** me into believing that this factory is not polluting the air because I am one of those

   people who is working to protect the environment. _____

5. It was **her** theory that led them to try using steam as a source of energy. _____

6. Bill tried to persuade Greta to join his political party, but she was not willing to leave her own just

   on the advice of a friend. _____

7. The decision to have an operation on the **disc** in her back was left totally to the patient.

   _____

8. I can't find the **exit** because the design of this store is so involved that I keep running into more

   display counters. _____

9. With all these figures in front of me, I don't know **at** what point I'll find a solution.

   _____

10. A gold bracelet is not only beautiful, but **it** is also a good value in today's market.

   _____

Word Skills

Name _____ Date _____

Writing

Imagine you are going to be the host of a party. You want to present your guests with healthful, tasty foods.

Write a paragraph in which you describe the menu you would plan for your party.

• What healthful foods would you serve to your guests?
• Why would you include each choice?

Use some vocabulary words from this unit in your writing.

_____

_____

_____

_____

_____

_____

_____

_____

_____

_____

_____

_____

_____

_____

Triangle of Mystery

Read the selection. Think about the meanings of the **boldfaced** words. Then go back to the selection. Underline the words or sentences that give you a clue to the meaning of each **boldfaced** word.

In a stretch of water between North and South America, the Atlantic Ocean and the Caribbean Sea meet. This region is referred to as "the Bermuda Triangle," after the nearby island of Bermuda. The mention of its name sends shivers down the spine of many a sailor and pilot.

Some people feel these fears are well founded, for the Bermuda Triangle has had more than its share of unexplained catastrophes. They **acknowledge**, or admit, that this spot has over the years been the site of a series of strange—even **bizarre**—disappearances.

For example, in 1969, a pilot sent an odd communication to the control tower. She was circling over two islands, yet she could not see them. On one island, a group of hotel guests watched and waited expectantly for her to land. She disappeared shortly afterward, and no trace of her or the aircraft was ever found. Everyone was **perplexed**, puzzled because the pilot had seen absolutely nothing below her, yet the people on the ground could clearly see her plane.

Other pilots have had their **perceptions** altered in the Bermuda Triangle and have seen strange things. Some have reported watching their instruments go wildly out of control on entering the Triangle. Even astronauts on space missions have claimed to see the area of the Triangle filled with huge foamy waves, waves that often signal great disturbances in nature.

These strange **circumstances**, or events, have led many people to **speculate** about what is causing these peculiar things to happen. Some writers have suggested the existence of a **mystical**, or supernatural, force that provides the energy to alter the real world.

Such explanations have led to disagreement. Most **oceanographic** scientists who study the world's seas believe that there is nothing unusual about the area. In their opinion, a disappearance is a **phenomenon**, or happening, that could occur anywhere in the world. That the Bermuda Triangle has had more than its share of disappearances they call an accident and purely **coincidental**. Yet belief in the Triangle's mystery persists. The fact remains that since 1854, more than fifty ships and airplanes have disappeared in or near the Bermuda Triangle. Most of them vanished without a trace.

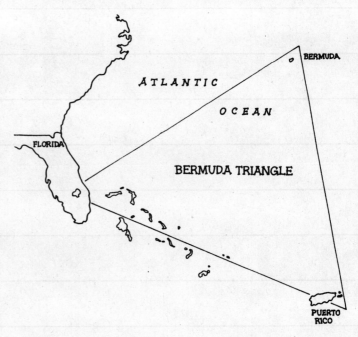

78

Context Clues

Meanings for the vocabulary words are given below. Go back to the selection and read each sentence that contains a vocabulary word. If you still cannot tell the meaning, look for clues in the sentences that come before and after the one with the vocabulary word. Write each word from the box before its meaning.

| coincidental | speculate | bizarre | oceanographic | phenomenon |
| perplexed | circumstances | acknowledge | perceptions | mystical |

1. _____ : recognize a claim or truth about something; admit

2. _____ : puzzled; confused

3. _____ : relating to events happening at the same time apparently by chance, but seeming somehow planned

4. _____ : extremely strange

5. _____ : observations made through the use of the senses

6. _____ : existing conditions

7. _____ : think about carefully; guess

8. _____ : an event that can be observed

9. _____ : having to do with the study of the ocean or sea

10. _____ : mysterious; having some secret meaning

www.harcourtschoolsupply.com

Name _____   Date _____

Analogies

An analogy compares two pairs of words. The relationship between the first pair of words is the same as the relationship between the second pair of words. Use the vocabulary words below to complete the following analogies.

speculate	mystical	bizarre	acknowledge

1. *Delighted* is to *happy* as _____ is to *supernatural*.

2. *Rare* is to *common* as _____ is to *ordinary*.

3. *Accept* is to *refuse* as _____ is to *deny*.

4. *Mix* is to *combine* as _____ is to *consider*.

Cloze Paragraphs

Use the words in the box to complete the fictional passage. Then reread the passage to be sure it makes sense.

circumstances	phenomenon	bizarre	speculated	perplexed	mystical

Have you ever witnessed an almost unexplainable (1) _____? Has anyone ever told you about a strange experience he or she has had? My friend Mike told me about a strange experience he had.

Under unusual (2) _____, Mike once flew a sick child across the Bermuda Triangle in his airplane. Mike had (3) _____ that, with clear skies, he could land in two hours. Then, without warning, a (4) _____ thing happened. The plane began to shake, and the needles on the instrument went out of control. Mike became frightened as he tried to keep the plane steady. He was totally (5) _____. Was there some

(6) _____ force out there that would not allow him to complete his flight?

Word Pairs

Words with similar parts may have related meanings. Study each word pair. Think about how the meanings of the words are alike. Check the meanings in the glossary. Then write a sentence for each word.

1. perplexing—perplexed

_____

_____

2. circumstances—circumstantial

_____

_____

3. coincide—coincidental

_____

_____

4. phenomenon—phenomenal

_____

_____

5. acknowledge—acknowledgement

_____

_____

6. oceanography—oceanographic

_____

_____

7. perceptions—perceive

_____

_____

Vocabulary in Context

Name _____   Date _____

The Latin Root *spec*

The Latin root *spec* comes from the Latin word *specere*, meaning "to look at" or "to see." Use your knowledge of this root word to help you find the correct word from the box for each clue. Write the word on the line.

spectacles	speculative	specimen	specter	spectator

1. A person watching a football game is called this: _____

2. This is something a biology teacher might show to teach students: _____

3. This is another word for a ghost: _____

4. These are something you wear to correct your eyesight: _____

5. If you have a habit of thinking a lot about things, you might be described as this:

   _____

Challenge Yourself

1. Name two things that might be studied by an <u>oceanographic</u> study group.

   _____

2. Name two <u>circumstances</u> that would prevent you from going swimming.

   _____

3. Name a time when you had to <u>acknowledge</u> you were wrong.

   _____

   _____

Standardized Test Practice

Circle the letter of the word that best completes the sentence.

TIP

Try reading the sentence with each answer choice. This will help you choose an answer that makes sense.

1. The mask that Jan wore was very strange. It looked _____.

   A coincidental   C pleasant

   B bizarre   D silent

2. My neighbor and I ran into each other in another city. It was purely _____.

   A coincidental   C oceanographic

   B important   D critical

3. The heavy rain flooded the field, and the ground was muddy. Under these _____, the game could not be played.

   A athletes   C perceptions

   B circumstances   D opponents

4. The woman studies animals and plants in the sea. She is a(n) _____ scientist.

   A easygoing   C mystical

   B oceanographic   D ancient

5. I felt as though I had been in that house before. It was a(n) _____ experience.

   A mystical   C fragile

   B oceanographic   D carved

6. We admit that we broke the rules. We _____ our mistake.

   A speculate   C reward

   B wonder   D acknowledge

7. Millions of butterflies migrate south every year. It is an annual _____.

   A celebration   C planet

   B perception   D phenomenon

8. The child couldn't figure out how to do the puzzle. She was completely _____.

   A perplexed   C retrieved

   B captured   D bizarre

9. In the desert, it is hard to judge distances. Your _____ may be thrown off.

   A phenomenon   C perceptions

   B emotions   D cactus

10. The experiment did not work. We can only _____ as to why it failed.

   A decide   C acknowledge

   B revise   D speculate

Vocabulary in Context

Understanding Related Words

The words in the box can be thematically related to the selection you read. They are used here in sentences about another wonder of nature—the Grand Canyon. See how many of the words you already know. Use the glossary to find the definitions of unfamiliar words.

brink	chasm	clefts	desolate	embedded
erosion	interior	plateau	protrude	receded

Use context clues to help you choose the word from the box that best completes each sentence. Write the word on the line.

1. To stand at the _____, or edge, of a cliff and look down into the Grand Canyon is to look back into more than a billion years of history.

2. The Grand Canyon had its origins in layers of rock deep in Earth's _____, which were pushed upward by earthquakes and volcanoes.

3. These rock layers were covered by ancient seas until the waters _____, or pulled back.

4. This caused the massive rock to _____ above the earth's surface in an area that is now part of the state of Arizona.

5. A huge _____ had been formed that looked like a giant stone layer cake.

6. The process of _____, the wearing away of rock by the wind, water, and sand, cut shapes and paths in the plateau.

7. Clues in the form of fossils of long-dead sharks and shellfish _____ in the rock have given scientists information about the canyon's history.

8. Scientists looked into small _____, or cracks, where these fossils were found enclosed in the ten-million-year-old rock.

9. It was John Wesley Powell who looked down into the _____ and felt that the only word for it was grand.

10. With all its visitors, the Grand Canyon will never be a _____ place.

84

Word Origins

Remember that knowing the origin of a word can help you understand its meaning. Read each word origin. Then write each word from the box next to its origin.

cleft	plateau	desolate	recede
chasm	erosion	protrude	

1. from the French *platel*, meaning "flat object": _____

2. from the Latin *erosion*, meaning "gnawing away": _____

3. from the Old English *clyft*, meaning "split": _____

4. from the Latin *recedere*, meaning "go" or "fall back": _____

5. from the Latin *desolare*, meaning "to make lonely": _____

6. from the Latin *pro + trudere*, meaning "to thrust": _____

7. from the Greek *cha + (a)sma*, meaning "to gape": _____

Using Analogies

An analogy compares two pairs of words. The relationship between the first pair of words is the same as the relationship between the second pair of words. Use the words in the box to complete the following analogies.

plateau	interior	recede	brink	chasm

1. *Middle* is to *center* as *edge* is to _____.

2. *Under* is to *below* as *inside* is to _____.

3. *Small* is to *cleft* as *huge* is to _____.

4. *Rounded* is to *hill* as *flat* is to _____.

5. *Progress* is to *advance* as *retreat* is to _____.

Word Skills

Name _____ Date _____

Synonyms

Choose the word or phrase that is a synonym, a word that has the same or almost the same meaning as the capitalized word. Write the letter of the correct word on the line.

_____ **1. PLATEAU**

     A flat rock   **B** slope   **C** peak   **D** cleft

_____ **2. EROSION**

     A planting   **B** an adding to   **C** a wearing away   **D** growing

_____ **3. CHASM**

     A river   **B** opening   **C** voice   **D** plateau

_____ **4. RECEDED**

     A advanced   **B** raised   **C** pulled back   **D** poured in

_____ **5. CLEFTS**

     A plateaus   **B** bridges   **C** fossils   **D** cracks

_____ **6. BRINK**

     A bottom   **B** edge   **C** request   **D** top

_____ **7. INTERIOR**

     A outside   **B** inside   **C** top   **D** bottom

_____ **8. PROTRUDE**

     A miss out   **B** shut out   **C** fall out   **D** stick out

_____ **9. DESOLATE**

     A deserted   **B** delicate   **C** busy   **D** mystical

_____ **10. EMBEDDED**

     A slept   **B** enclosed   **C** floated   **D** receded

Word Skills

Vocabulary in Context G8, SV 9780547625812

Writing

Write a paragraph expressing your views about the reason for the disappearances in the Bermuda Triangle.

• Do you believe that the disappearances within the Bermuda Triangle are just coincidental?
• Or do you think some unusual force of nature has played a part in those events?
• What are your reasons for your beliefs?

Use some vocabulary words from this unit in your writing.

_____
_____
_____
_____
_____
_____
_____
_____
_____
_____
_____
_____
_____
_____
_____
_____

A Puzzle Built of Stones

Read the selection. Think about the meanings of the **boldfaced** words. Then go back to the selection. Underline the words or sentences that give you a clue to the meaning of each **boldfaced** word.

Every year tourists and other **sightseers** from around the world come to Salisbury Plain in Wiltshire, England, to see one of the earth's most mysterious monuments—Stonehenge. This series of huge stones standing in a semicircle has puzzled people for generations. Who put them there, how did they do it, and why?

Some of these questions have been easier to answer than others. Scientists have determined the age of the monuments by using **radiocarbon**, a substance contained in the stones. They have acquired much new information. The **revelations** have been amazing. The studies show that the monument and some of the symbols etched on the stones may be between two and three thousand years old. Although some of the stones are missing, most of the ancient structure is still **intact**.

The placement of the stones has led scientists to some conclusions. One stone marker, for example, is positioned about 250 feet east of the altar. The reason for this becomes clear on June 21, the summer **solstice**. On this longest day of the year, the sun and the stone marker are in perfect **alignment**. Because of this arrangement in a straight line, the marker casts a shadow on the altar at dawn.

Furthermore, after studying drawings of the altar, scientists drew lines connecting various parts of the structure. The **symmetry**, or balance, of these lines suggests that Stonehenge may have served as a gigantic calendar to predict the seasons of the year and eclipses of the sun and the moon.

All this evidence seems to **imply**, or suggest, that Stonehenge was built by ancient Britons who practiced **astrology**, the belief that the stars can influence human events. The altar may have been used for **rites** and ceremonies related to astrology and sun worship.

The beliefs of these people must have been very strong to motivate them to move these huge stones to Salisbury Plain. The biggest stones stand thirteen feet high and weigh about fifty thousand pounds each. In an age before machinery, it must have taken a tremendous human effort to transport them. How did they do it? This is another of the questions that remain unanswered about this puzzle built of stone.

Context Clues

Read each sentence. Look for clues to help you complete each sentence with a word from the box. Write the word on the line.

intact	symmetry	alignment	solstice	rites
sightseers	revelations	astrology	imply	radiocarbon

1. Stonehenge is a popular place that tourists and other _____ visit every year.

2. They are amazed that the ancient monument is still _____, or whole, after so many years.

3. Scientists used a substance within the stones called _____ to determine the age of the stones.

4. According to the extraordinary _____ of scientists, parts of Stonehenge may be 3,000 years old.

5. The scientific evidence seems to _____, or suggest, that the ancient Britons believed that the positions of the planets and stars influence people's lives.

6. On the longest day of the year, the summer _____, something strange happens at Stonehenge.

7. The _____ of the sun and a certain stone marker is so perfect that a shadow is cast on the altar.

8. Many people believe that Stonehenge was used as a giant calendar because the _____, or balance, of the stones may have made it possible to predict the seasons.

9. Certain ceremonies, or _____, may have been performed by ancient Britons at the altar of Stonehenge.

10. These people of long ago believed in _____, the belief that the positions of the planets and stars control and influence people's lives.

Vocabulary in Context

Tangled-Up Words

In the following passage, the underlined words do not make sense. But each sounds similar to a word in the box. Study the context in which the underlined words appear. For each word, find the word in the box that should be used in its place. Write the correct word on the numbered line.

intact	symmetry	alignment	solstice	rites
sightseers	revelations	astrology	imply	radiocarbon

How many (1) signatures visit Stonehenge each year? The answer is many because the (2) intone stones in their perfect (3) assignment amaze all who view them.

Most people try to see this amazing ruin on the summer (4) surface. It is at that time that a shadow cast directly over the altar reveals the (5) symphony of the stones. The size of the stones and the spectacle they create (6) deny that the people who erected these stones were more knowledgeable than we would expect.

What were some of the special (7) riots the ancient people of Stonehenge observed? We do not know the answer to this question, but we know that they were, in part, based on (8) astonishing—the study of the planets and the stars by those who believe they influence human behavior.

The process of dating objects with the use of (9) radiology allows scientists to find out the age of ancient ruins on the earth. Our technology leads to (10) realizations about the wisdom of people from the past.

1. _____   6. _____

2. _____   7. _____

3. _____   8. _____

4. _____   9. _____

5. _____   10. _____

Vocabulary in Context

Name _____ Date _____

Analogies

An analogy compares two pairs of words. The relationship between the first pair of words is the same as the relationship between the second pair of words. Use the words in the box to complete the following analogies.

sightseers	astrology	intact	imply	revelations

1. *Try* is to *attempt* as _____ is to *suggest*.

2. *Empty* is to *full* as *broken* is to _____.

3. *Caves* are to *speleology* as *stars* are to _____.

4. *Fans* are to *football* as _____ are to *monuments*.

5. *Displays* are to *exhibits* as *discoveries* are to _____.

Rewriting Sentences

Rewrite each sentence using one of the words from the box.

radiocarbon	symmetry	solstice	alignment	rites

1. I visited Stonehenge on June 21, the longest day of the year.

_____

_____

2. We were told by a guide that the balanced arrangement of the stones may have made it possible for ancient Britons to predict eclipses.

_____

_____

3. The stone altar may have served for ceremonies relating to astrology.

_____

_____

Figures of Speech

Writers use **figures of speech** to add interest to their writing. **Personification** is a figure of speech that gives human characteristics to an animal or a thing. **Similes** are figures of speech that compare two unlike things to show how they are alike. Similes make comparisons using the words *like* or *as*.

Decide whether each statement about Stonehenge includes an example of personification or a simile. Write the correct answer on the line.

1. The enormous stones silently greet the curious tourists.   _____

2. The stones stand like giant ambassadors from the past.   _____

3. Overcome by emotion, the tourists point and stare in silent amazement, like children seeing their favorite character at Disneyland for the first time.   _____

4. On the morning of the longest day of the year, the marker greeted the sun and cast her shadow over the altar, sheltering ancient peoples as they performed their rites.   _____

5. Scientists study Stonehenge like detectives at a crime scene, looking for clues that will help them better understand this mysterious place.   _____

Word Groups

As you read each pair of words, think about how they are alike. Write the word from the box that best completes each group.

imply	revelations	sightseers	intact	symmetry

1. whole, unbroken, _____

2. tourists, visitors, _____

3. balance, evenness, _____

4. eye-openers, surprises, _____

5. suggest, mean, _____

Standardized Test Practice

Circle the letter of the word that best completes the sentence.

TIP

Before you choose an answer, try reading the sentence with each answer choice. This will help you choose an answer that makes sense.

1. The planets and stars are very important to those who believe in _____.

   A astrology   C science

   B radiocarbon   D monuments

2. The _____ suggests Stonehenge was a calendar.

   A puzzles   C radiocarbon

   B symmetry   D substances

3. The scientists used _____ to tell the age of the stones.

   A solstice   C radiocarbon

   B astrology   D calendars

4. The scientists uncovered some surprising _____ about Stonehenge and shared them with historians and journalists.

   A symmetry   C revelations

   B pounds   D circles

5. The _____ took a tour of the countryside.

   A revelations   C rocks

   B sightseers   D carbons

6. Her tone of voice seems to _____ that she is angry.

   A remember   C intact

   B wonder   D imply

7. The telephone pole and the tree were in perfect _____.

   A solstice   C alignment

   B intact   D summer

8. The cup remained _____ after it hit the floor.

   A rites   C symmetry

   B intact   D revelations

9. Special _____ were performed to honor the hero.

   A sightseers   C astrology

   B rites   D revelations

10. The sun sets late on the summer _____.

   A week   C winter

   B symmetry   D solstice

Vocabulary in Context

93

Understanding Related Words

The words in the box can be thematically related to the selection you read. They are used here in sentences about the study of past cultures. See how many of the words you already know. Use the glossary to find the definitions of unfamiliar words.

archaeologists	bonanza	characteristic	continuity	cultural
descriptive	engravings	excavate	frequency	reverence

In each sentence below, a word or phrase is underlined. Choose a word from the box to replace that word or phrase. Use the glossary to look up any unfamiliar words. Write the word on the line.

1. Scientists who study the ancient past are interested in people and how they lived.

   _____

2. They must have patience, for sometimes they will dig up vast areas of ground before finding a single

   relic. _____

3. Other times, they may be lucky and find many objects that are a source of great fortune in terms of

   providing information about the past. _____

4. Often objects will provide information about a people's activities that are related to customs, arts, and

   beliefs. _____

5. Scientists always hope to find objects that are typical of a particular people.

   _____

6. When an object is found with repeated occurrence, then scientists can be sure it is typical.

   _____

7. Objects that are able to tell about a people are the most valuable to scientists.

   _____

8. Also valuable are pictures that have been etched in stone or metal. _____

9. These pictures often show a people's deep respect for nature or for a particular god or hero.

   _____

10. They may also show signs of a condition of going on without stopping from the past to the present.

   _____

Word Skills

Using Analogies

An analogy compares two pairs of words. The relationship between the first pair of words is the same as the relationship between the second pair of words. Use the words in the box to complete the following analogies.

excavate	reverence	characteristic	engravings
archaeologists	bonanza	continuity	

1. *Strange* is to *unusual* as _____ is to *typical*.

2. *Ruin* is to *misfortune* as _____ is to *fortune*.

3. *Admiration* is to *love* as _____ is to *respect*.

4. *Dentists* are to *doctors* as _____ are to *scientists*.

5. *Pull* is to *tug* as _____ is to *dig*.

6. *Oaks* are to *trees* as _____ are to *drawings*.

7. *Day* is to *night* as _____ is to *change*.

Cloze Paragraph

Use the words in the box to complete the passage. Then reread the passage to be sure it makes sense.

cultural	engravings	frequency	continuity	descriptive	archaeologists

In many places around the world, (1) _____ looking for the remains of

the ancient peoples have found cave paintings. Sometimes the paintings are painted on the walls, and

sometimes they are (2) _____ that have been etched in stone. But no matter how

they are done, the paintings are (3) _____ of the way a group lived in ancient

times. The paintings show gods and heroes. They also show holidays, ceremonies, and other important

parts of the (4) _____ life of the people. The old cave paintings are discovered

with (5) _____. Through time, these paintings show that there is some

(6) _____ in the way people express themselves.

Word Skills

Sentence Completion

Read each sentence carefully. Then choose the best answer to complete each sentence. Write the letter of the answer you have chosen on the line.

_____ 1. When you *excavate* to find treasure, you _____ for it.

    A shop   **B** chop   **C** dig   **D** bargain

_____ 2. A box with *engravings* has _____ etched in it.

    A liquids   **B** jewels   **C** pictures   **D** stones

_____ 3. *Archaeologists* would be looking for old _____ from the past.

    A people   **B** relics   **C** moons   **D** trees

_____ 4. A discovery that can be called a *bonanza* will make someone _____.

    A poor   **B** rich   **C** tired   **D** wary

_____ 5. A *characteristic* trait is one that is _____.

    A unusual   **B** frightening   **C** dangerous   **D** typical

_____ 6. A *descriptive* poem gives a _____ picture.

    A song   **B** word   **C** sad   **D** long

_____ 7. To get *continuity* in your writing, you must _____ your thoughts.

    A connect   **B** display   **C** remove   **D** ignore

_____ 8. In *reverence*, he _____ to the king.

    A waved   **B** sprinted   **C** sailed   **D** bowed

_____ 9. A person whom you see *with frequency* is someone you see _____.

    A a lot   **B** seldom   **C** occasionally   **D** today

_____ 10. A visit to a _____ could be called a *cultural* experience.

    A zoo   **B** doctor   **C** planetarium   **D** museum

Word Skills

Writing

No one can explain how the huge stones were moved to Salisbury Plain. Do you have any ideas about how these huge stones were moved?

- Could they have been rolled over logs?
- Could they have been dragged across the land by thousands of people using ropes?
- Did the people have gigantic wheelbarrows?

Write a paragraph telling your ideas. Explain what methods you think the ancient Britons used. Remember that this was an age before machinery. Use some vocabulary words from this unit in your writing.

_____

_____

_____

_____

_____

_____

_____

_____

_____

_____

_____

_____

_____

Photographs of the Future

Read the selection. Think about the meanings of the **boldfaced** words. Then go back to the selection. Underline the words or sentences that give you a clue to the meaning of each **boldfaced** word.

A missing child is a parent's worst nightmare. Parents can keep current photographs and fingerprints to assist in the **identification** of their children. But imagine a situation in which a fifteen-month-old boy disappears and is still missing at age six, **despite** relentless efforts by police and other agencies. Not too long ago, this would have been a real **dilemma** for authorities conducting the search. The difficulty was looking for a six-year-old by using a picture that was more than four years old.

Fortunately for parents today, there is hope. In 1984, the National Center for Missing and Exploited Children, or NCMEC, was established **primarily** to help coordinate programs to find missing children. To fulfill this main function, NCMEC keeps a data bank on missing children throughout the country, maintains a toll-free hotline for reports and leads, and distributes posters of missing children.

NCMEC artists have used computers and sophisticated software that reproduce children's growth patterns. The resulting images help searchers **envision** how a child who disappeared several years ago might look today. The process begins when an artist or technician scans the most recent photograph or picture of the missing child onto the screen. For example, it might be a photograph of a fifteen-month-old boy. Over hours or days, the child's face will undergo a remarkable **transformation**, again from fifteen months to, say, six years. Using computer programs, NCMEC artists can merge certain features from childhood photos of the child's parents, lengthen the face, and adjust any of the hundreds of thousands of tiny graphic units on the screen, called pixels, one by one, in two-inch sections at a time. The artist will work with facial **components** to make changes. The nose and ears might be made longer and the lips fuller, the chin might be sharpened, teeth might be added, and cheekbones defined. When the process is finished, the child will look like his mother, his father, and himself. The image is a **projection** of what the child might look like now. Although the changes are only "imagined" by the computer, such **alterations** have proven to be highly accurate in several cases.

Similar technology is being used in **criminology** to help police "update" photographs of criminals who have had plastic surgery. Computer technology is invaluable for police and for families of missing children.

Name _____ Date _____

Context Clues

Read each sentence. Look for clues to help you complete each sentence with a word from the box. Write the word on the line.

projection	identification	alterations	dilemma	despite
primarily	transformation	criminology	envision	components

1. Fingerprints and photographs are two forms of _____ used by police officers trying to locate missing children.

2. Computers have been used in the field of _____ to identify criminals who may have changed their appearance in some way.

3. By "imagining" a future, a computer can create a _____ of what someone might look like one day.

4. This allows a computer to _____, or picture, how a person's face might change or age over the years.

5. The computer makes _____, or changes, to show how the features on a person's face might change with time.

6. The end result is a _____, or change, of the original photograph.

7. Using computers to work with photographs is only one of many _____, or parts, in a nationwide effort to locate missing children.

8. Computers are _____ used to project future pictures of children who have been missing for many years.

9. A complete solution cannot be offered by computers, _____ the amazing work they do.

10. Police departments still face the _____, or problem, of locating a child who could be anywhere.

Name _____ Date _____

Word Groups

As you read each pair of words, think about how they are alike. Write the word from the box that completes each group.

alterations	**components**	**envision**	**dilemma**

1. problem, conflict, _____

2. changes, substitutions, _____

3. parts, pieces, _____

4. picture, imagine, _____

Rewriting Sentences

Rewrite each sentence using one of the vocabulary words from the box.

identification	**despite**	**transformation**	**projection**	**primarily**	**criminology**

1. The use of computers in the field that studies criminals is helpful.

_____

2. Computer art can help to provide evidence of who someone is, after that person has gone through physical changes.

_____

_____

3. Within a few seconds, a photo of a child can undergo a complete change.

_____

_____

4. Although the image created is only a prediction based on known information, it seems that the changes are often quite accurate.

_____

_____

Crossword Puzzle

Use the words in the box and the clues to complete the crossword puzzle.

identification	projection	alterations	dilemma	despite
primarily	transformation	criminology	envision	components

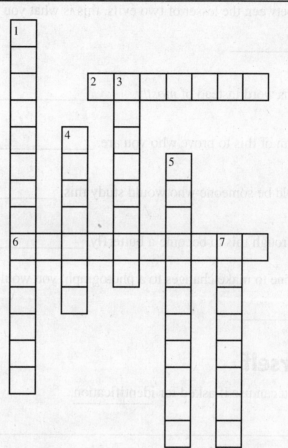

Across

2. in spite of
6. parts
8. mostly
9. study of crime and criminals
10. prediction

Down

1. recognition
3. imagine
4. problem
5. changes
7. complete change

Word Game

Read each clue. Then write the word from the box that fits the clue.

alterations	transformation	dilemma	primarily	identification	criminology

1. If you must choose between the lesser of two evils, this is what you face.

   _____

2. You can often use this word instead of *mostly*. _____

3. You must show a form of this to prove who you are. _____

4. A police officer would be someone who would study this. _____

5. A caterpillar goes through this to become a butterfly. _____

6. If you wanted someone to make changes to a photograph, you would ask for these.

   _____

Challenge Yourself

1. Name two things you can use if asked for identification.

   _____

2. Name one transformation you have seen.

   _____

3. Name a dilemma you have solved recently.

   _____

Vocabulary in Context

Name _____ Date _____

Standardized Test Practice

Circle the letter of the best answer to complete each sentence.

This test will show how well you understand the meaning of the vocabulary words. Think about the meaning of the italicized word before you choose your answer.

1. *Criminology* is the study of _____ and its prevention.

   A history   C crime

   B photography   D computer science

2. To *envision* something means to _____ it in your mind.

   A forget   C whisper

   B picture   D erase

3. To make *alterations* means to make _____.

   A colors   C altars

   B standards   D changes

4. *Despite* is a word that means _____.

   A in spite of   C on the top of

   B in a minute   D before

5. The tadpole went through a *transformation* to become a _____.

   A frog   C giraffe

   B cat   D worm

6. A *dilemma* is a _____ with no simple solution.

   A problem   C prediction

   B sign   D removal

7. The police officer showed her _____ for *identification*.

   A food   C amusement

   B badge   D window

8. When you make a *projection*, you are thinking about the _____.

   A future   C spaces

   B sizes   D tension

9. A *component* is a _____ of something.

   A whole   C part

   B color   D persuasion

10. To be *primarily* concerned means to care _____ about a certain thing.

    A never   C always

    B rarely   D mainly

    Vocabulary in Context G8, SV 9780547625812

Name _____ Date _____

Understanding Related Words

The words in the box are thematically related to the selection you read. They are used here in sentences about computers. See how many of the words you already know. Use the glossary to find the definitions of unfamiliar words.

access	alternative	automatically	capability	electronic
limitless	manipulate	monitor	quantity	storage

In each sentence below, a word is missing. Use context clues to choose a word from the box to complete the sentence. Write the word on the line.

1. Today, computers of all shapes and sizes, at home or in an office, can perform a number of difficult tasks quickly and _____.

2. The programs that a computer keeps in _____ allow it to perform its many different functions.

3. Often, a special command allows the user _____ to these programs.

4. Today's computers, run by _____ parts, are easy and inexpensive for an individual to operate.

5. You might be surprised by the seemingly _____, or infinite, number of tasks a home computer can perform.

6. A computer has the _____ to do tasks instantly that would take a person a long time.

7. My family uses our computer to calculate and _____ our daily expenses.

8. Our neighbors have a large _____ of games.

9. Good instructions can help someone easily _____, or use, most computer parts correctly within a short period of time.

10. Do you think a future _____ to the computer will be invented sometime soon?

Word Skills

Synonyms

Remember that synonyms are words that have the same or almost the same meaning. Write a word from the box that is a synonym of the italicized word in each sentence.

quantity	monitor	capability	manipulate	limitless

1. A computer made twenty years ago has nowhere near the *power* or the _____
of a computer now.

2. Today, uses for computers are almost as *endless* as the seemingly _____
tasks they can perform.

3. Computers can be programmed to *check* the workings of a space shuttle and

   _____ a person's heart rate.

4. Computers can remember a great *amount* of information and print out a huge

   _____ of it in seconds.

5. Yet computers can be so easy to *use* that children can _____ them without
a problem.

Cloze Paragraph

Use the words in the box to complete the passage. Then reread the passage to be sure it makes sense.

automatically	electronic	storage	access	alternatives

In order to (1) _____ a computer program, you may need to know the password.

Once you have gained entry to the program, it can perform tasks (2) _____. Many

programs have a menu that offers (3) _____. Information that is entered can be put

in (4) _____ so that it can be recalled later. A computer is indeed a marvelous

(5) _____ machine!

Word Skills

Name _____   Date _____

Word Map

Use the words in the box to complete the word map about computers. Add other words that you know to each group. One heading will not have any words from the box, but only your words.

electronic	storage	limitless	capability
quantity	automatically	access	

How Computers Operate

1. _____
2. _____
3. _____
4. _____
5. _____

What Computers Do

1. _____
2. _____
3. _____
4. _____
5. _____

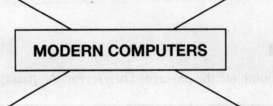

MODERN COMPUTERS

How Computers Work Better Than People

1. _____
2. _____
3. _____
4. _____
5. _____

Subjects of Computer Games

1. _____
2. _____
3. _____
4. _____
5. _____

Unit 10
Vocabulary in Context G8, SV 9780547625812

Word Skills

Name _____ Date _____

Writing

You are an inventor who has just completed work on a new computer program. Write a paragraph describing your invention.

- What does your computer program do?
- Who will be interested in using the program?
- How can your invention make people's lives better or more fun?

Use some vocabulary words from this unit in your writing.

_____

_____

_____

_____

_____

_____

_____

_____

_____

_____

_____

_____

Glossary

A

absorption	*noun*	the process by which food enters the bloodstream after it has been broken down (page 68)
access	*noun*	the chance or right to approach or use (page 104)
accuracy	*noun*	the state of being correct and exact (page 54)
achieve	*verb*	to accomplish (page 64)
achievements	*noun*	accomplishments (page 58)
acknowledge	*verb*	to recognize a claim or truth about something; to admit (page 78)
acknowledgement	*noun*	the act of recognizing a claim or truth about something; the act of admitting (page 81)
acquired	*verb*	got, came to have as one's own (page 58)
acquisition	*noun*	purchase; something one gets (page 64)
adequately	*adverb*	sufficiently; well enough (page 18)
affliction	*noun*	illness (page 48)
alcoves	*noun*	small recessed sections of rooms (page 38)
alignment	*noun*	arrangement in a straight line (page 88)
alterations	*noun*	changes (page 98)
alternative	*noun*	another possibility (page 104)
analyze	*verb*	to study carefully (page 44)
anticipate	*verb*	to know beforehand; to expect (page 54)
application	*noun*	use; the act of putting something on or putting something to use (pages 18, 29)
apply	*verb*	to make a formal request, usually in writing (page 34)
archaeologists	*noun*	scientists who study relics from the ancient past (page 94)
arterial	*adjective*	related to the tube carrying blood (the artery); constituting a main route in a road (page 34)
artery	*noun*	a main road; a tube that carries blood away from the heart to the other parts of the body (page 29)
ascertain	*verb*	to learn; to find out (page 44)
associated	*verb*	connected (page 9)
association	*noun*	connection; organization (page 14)
astrology	*noun*	the study of the stars and planets by those who believe they influence human behavior (page 88)
atypical	*adjective*	not normal (page 64)
automated	*adjective*	operated, controlled, or worked by a machine (page 24)
automatically	*adverb*	done without outside help (page 104)
avert	*verb*	to prevent; to avoid (page 54)

B

bankrupt	*adjective*	broke; out of money (page 8)
bankruptcy	*noun*	the state of being out of money (page 14)
bizarre	*adjective*	extremely strange (page 78)
bonanza	*noun*	something that brings wealth or happiness (page 94)

brink	*noun*	edge of a steep place (page 84)

C

calories	*noun*	units used to measure the amount of energy supplied by various foods (page 68)
capability	*noun*	the ability to do work (page 104)
carbohydrates	*noun*	chemical compounds such as starches and sugars (page 68)
characteristic	*adjective*	typical; making a person, group, or thing different or distinct (page 94)
chasm	*noun*	deep canyon, deep crack (page 84)
circumstances	*noun*	the conditions surrounding an event (page 78)
circumstantial	*adjective*	depending on the conditions surrounding an event (page 81)
clefts	*noun*	openings; cracks (page 84)
clinical	*adjective*	having to do with the treatment of patients (page 48)
coincide	*verb*	to happen at the same time (page 81)
coincidental	*adjective*	relating to events happening at the same time apparently by chance, but seeming somehow planned (page 78)
commodity	*noun*	anything bought and sold (page 74)
compensate	*verb*	to make up for; to make an equal payment for (page 74)
compensation	*noun*	payment or something else given for pay for work done, loss, or damage; something that makes up for something else (page 75)
complex	*adjective*	difficult to understand (page 75)
complexity	*noun*	the quality of being difficult to understand or complicated (page 74)
components	*noun*	parts (page 98)
compute	*verb*	to figure out by using mathematics (page 54)
conservationists	*noun*	people who work to protect and save natural resources (page 74)
consolation	*noun*	comfort (page 48)
constructive	*adjective*	helpful (page 18)
consume	*verb*	to eat or drink; to use up (page 68)
consumed	*verb*	used up; eaten (page 28)
consumer	*noun*	person who uses or buys (page 34)
contemporary	*adjective*	belonging to today (page 24)
contend	*verb*	to compete; to clash (page 29)
contention	*noun*	argument (page 34)
continuity	*noun*	the state of being uninterrupted; a connection that remains unbroken over time (page 94)
contributor	*noun*	person who gives knowledge, time, or money (page 54)
controversial	*adjective*	causing questions and arguments (page 44)
convenience	*noun*	freedom from difficulty (page 24)
conversion	*noun*	the act of changing; turning from one thing into another (page 74)
corrode	*verb*	to wear away by the action of chemicals (page 35)
corrosion	*noun*	a wearing away by the action of chemicals (page 29)
corrosive	*adjective*	able to wear away by the action of chemicals (page 34)
cosmos	*noun*	all of space; the universe (page 44)
counterclockwise	*adverb*	in a direction opposite of the normal movement of a clock (page 18)

criminology	noun	the study of crime and criminals (page 98)
cultural	adjective	having to do with all the beliefs and activities of a particular group of people (page 94)

D

defect	noun; verb	fault or deficiency; to desert one's country; to abandon a cause or group, often to support another (pages 58, 62)
defective	adjective	faulty (page 64)
deficiency	noun	shortage; a lack of something required (page 68)
dejected	adjective	sad (page 36)
descriptive	adjective	giving a picture of; showing (page 94)
desolate	adjective	deserted; without inhabitants (page 84)
despair	noun	hopelessness (page 64)
desperate	adjective	urgent; without hope (page 59)
desperation	noun	hopelessness (page 64)
despite	preposition	in spite of (page 98)
devastate	verb	to ruin; to destroy (page 54)
devoted	adjective	dedicated to some purpose, activity, or person (page 9)
devotion	noun	dedication to a purpose, activity, or person (page 14)
diagnosis	noun	a medical opinion about a person's health (page 48)
diameter	noun	a straight line passing through the center of a circle from one side to the other (page 28)
digestion	noun	the process by which the body breaks down food in the stomach to use as energy (page 68)
dilemma	noun	a difficult problem; a situation requiring a choice between two evils (page 98)
discreet	adjective	wisely cautious; careful (page 75)
discretion	noun	freedom to act on one's own judgment; wise caution (page 74)
diverse	adjective	dissimilar (page 8)
diversity	noun	variety (page 14)
domestic	adjective	of one's home country (page 29)
drastic	adjective	extreme; harsh (page 8)
duplicated	verb	corresponded exactly, copied (page 59)
duplication	noun	a copy (page 64)

E

economical	adjective	thrifty (page 28)
economy	noun	financial system (page 35)
educator	noun	teacher (page 18)
efficiency	noun	the ability to produce a desired effect with the least effort or waste (page 34)
efficiently	adverb	producing a desired effect with the least effort or waste (page 28)
efficient	adjective	able to produce a desired effect with the least effort or waste (page 35)
eject	verb	to throw out; to force someone to leave (page 36)

electronic	*adjective*	working by electricity (page 104)
eligibility	*noun*	qualification (page 64)
eligible	*adjective*	qualified (page 58)
embedded	*adjective*	buried; set in (page 84)
emotion	*noun*	feeling (page 14)
emotional	*adjective*	related to feelings (page 9)
engravings	*noun*	pictures that are cut into a hard surface (page 94)
envision	*verb*	to form a picture of; to imagine (page 98)
enzymes	*noun*	chemical substances that help break down foods in the body (page 68)
erosion	*noun*	slow wearing away (page 84)
evaluate	*verb*	to measure; to judge (page 54)
excavate	*verb*	to dig up (page 94)
exclude	*verb*	to restrict (page 64)
exclusive	*adjective*	restrictive; belonging to a select group (page 59)
exist	*verb*	to be; to be real (page 35)
existence	*noun*	being (page 28)
experimental	*adjective*	having to do with ideas that are being tested; not yet proven (page 18)
exterior	*noun*	outside of a room or building (page 14)

F

falter	*verb*	to stumble; to hesitate (page 59)
features	*noun*	characteristics; special parts (page 38)
fiction	*noun*	an untruth; a literary work with imaginary characters or events (page 14)
fictional	*adjective*	imaginary; of a literary work with imaginary characters or events (page 9)
finance	*noun*	money matters (page 64)
financial	*adjective*	related to money matters (page 58)
financier	*noun*	a person who is skilled in money matters and has a lot of money (page 64)
flair	*noun*	a natural talent or ability; a sense of what is stylish (page 9)
flamboyant	*adjective*	flashy; extravagant (page 9)
frequency	*noun*	the number of times; how often (page 94)

G

geothermal	*adjective*	produced by heat within the earth (page 74)

H

hospitalized	*adjective*	in the hospital to receive treatment (page 48)
humanitarian	*noun*	a person who is actively concerned with promoting human welfare (page 9)
humorist	*noun*	a person skilled at telling jokes and funny stories (page 9)
humorous	*adjective*	funny (page 14)

I

identification	*noun*	the act of finding out who someone is; something used to prove who a person is (page 98)
immensity	*noun*	great size; enormity (page 44)
imply	*verb*	to suggest without being specific (page 88)
inadequate	*adjective*	not enough (page 54)
include	*verb*	to bring in (page 64)
individualist	*noun*	a person who is unique or nonconforming (page 14)
individualistic	*adjective*	unique; noncomforming (page 9)
ineligible	*adjective*	not qualified (page 64)
inevitable	*adjective*	certain to happen; not able to be avoided (page 44)
infinite	*adjective*	without limits; endless (page 44)
initiative	*noun*	willingness to try new things; ambition to take the lead (page 18)
inject	*verb*	to force or drive a liquid into something; to insert (page 36)
injection	*noun*	the forcing or driving of (a liquid) into something (page 29)
innovation	*noun*	something newly introduced (page 28)
inquire	*verb*	to question; to pry (pages 14, 64)
inquiry	*noun*	a question; an investigation (pages 14, 44)
inquisitive	*adjective*	questioning; curious; prying (page 8)
intact	*adjective*	whole; not broken (page 88)
integrates	*verb*	brings parts together into a whole (page 24)
interior	*noun*	inside (page 84)
interiors	*noun*	insides of a room or building (page 9)
invaluable	*adjective*	priceless (page 44)
iridescent	*adjective*	showing many colors that constantly change in the light (page 38)
isolate	*verb*	to set apart from others (page 29)
isolation	*noun*	the process of setting apart from others; remoteness from others (page 34)

L

landscape	*noun*	a stretch of natural scenery (page 38)
lethal	*adjective*	deadly (page 54)
limitless	*adjective*	without any end (page 104)

M

magnificence	*noun*	splendor; beauty (page 38)
maintain	*verb*	to keep something in good repair (page 64)
maintenance	*noun*	the work of keeping something in good repair (page 59)
malnutrition	*noun*	a condition in which the body suffers from a lack of nutritious substances (page 68)
manipulate	*verb*	to control; to work with the hands (page 104)
memorable	*adjective*	worth remembering (page 8)
memorize	*verb*	to commit to memory (page 14)
modem	*noun*	device for transmitting data from one computer to another (page 24)

monitor	*verb*	to check; to keep watch over (page 104)
monopolized	*verb*	got full possession or control of; dominated completely (page 59)
monopoly	*noun*	control (page 64)
mystical	*adjective*	mysterious; having some secret meaning (page 78)

N

neurology	*noun*	the branch of medicine that deals with the nervous system and its diseases (page 48)
nonfiction	*noun*	a written work about true events and real people (page 14)
nutrients	*noun*	nutritious substances that are necessary for proper body functioning (page 68)

O

obstacles	*noun*	barriers; things that get in the way or hinder (page 29)
oceanographic	*adjective*	having to do with the study of the ocean or sea (page 78)
oceanography	*noun*	the study of the ocean or sea (page 81)
optimistic	*adjective*	hopeful that things will turn out in the best possible way (page 48)
outlook	*noun*	viewpoint (page 58)
outmoded	*adjective*	dated; no longer useful or acceptable (page 24)

P

paralytic	*adjective*	unable to move (page 48)
pedestrian	*adjective*	dull; commonplace; of or for people who are walking (pages 58, 62)
pedestrian	*noun*	a person who is walking (page 62)
pediatrician	*noun*	a children's doctor (page 48)
perceive	*verb*	to use the senses to make observations (page 81)
perceptions	*noun*	observations made through the use of the senses (page 78)
perplexed	*adjective*	puzzled; confused (page 78)
perplexing	*adjective*	very difficult to understand or come to terms with (page 81)
phenomenon	*noun*	an event, especially one that is difficult to explain (page 78)
plateau	*noun*	a high, flat piece of land (page 84)
primarily	*adverb*	mainly; for the most part (page 98)
probe	*verb*	to explore (page 44)
procedures	*noun*	steps to be followed (page 29)
proceed	*verb*	to continue on; to go on (page 34)
project	*verb*	to forecast, to predict (page 36)
projection	*noun*	prediction; plan for the future (page 98)
prominence	*noun*	fame; importance (page 64)
prominent	*adjective*	noticeable; widely and favorably known (page 59)
proteins	*noun*	chemical compounds that contain nitrogen and are found in meat, milk, and fish (page 68)
protrude	*verb*	to stick out (page 84)
pursued	*verb*	chased, followed, or gone on with; aimed at (page 8)
pursuit	*noun*	a chase; an activity or interest (page 14)

Vocabulary in Context G8, SV 9780547625812

Q

quantity	*noun*	amount (page 104)

R

radiated	*verb*	spread out from a center in all directions (page 38)
radiocarbon	*noun*	a substance that can be measured to find out the ages of ancient objects (page 88)
receded	*verb*	pulled back; withdrew (page 84)
refine	*verb*	to produce a pure or fine form of a raw material; to improve (page 34)
refinement	*adjective*	elegance (page 35)
refinery	*noun*	a plant or establishment where a raw material, such as sugar cane, is made fine or pure (page 28)
reject	*verb*	to refuse (page 36)
relish	*noun*	a distinctive or appetizing flavor; great enjoyment or pleasure; a food such as pickles or olives (page 62)
relished	*verb*	enjoyed thoroughly (page 59)
replacements	*noun*	things that take the place of other things (page 24)
replenished	*verb*	filled again; furnished with a new supply (page 74)
require	*verb*	to need; to force (pages 14, 64)
requirement	*noun*	necessity (page 59)
revelations	*noun*	pieces of new information (page 88)
reverence	*noun*	deep respect (page 94)
revolutionized	*verb*	changed greatly (page 24)
rites	*noun*	ceremonies (page 88)
rural	*adjective*	of or like the country; rustic (page 8)

S

seismic	*adjective*	having to do with earthquakes (page 54)
sightseers	*noun*	people who visit a place of interest (page 88)
simplifying	*verb*	making easier (page 24)
solstice	*noun*	the two times each year that the direct rays of the sun are farthest away from the equator; June 21, the longest day of the year in the northern hemisphere, and December 22, the shortest day of the year in the northern hemisphere (page 88)
specimen	*noun*	an organism preserved as a typical example; a sample used for testing and diagnosis (page 82)
spectacles	*noun*	glasses (page 82)
spectator	*noun*	a viewer; observer (page 82)
specter	*noun*	a ghost (page 82)
speculate	*verb*	to think about carefully; to guess (page 78)
speculative	*adjective*	given to curiosity; given to forming conclusions not based on fact (page 82)
speleology	*noun*	the study and exploration of caves and their contents (page 38)
split second	*noun*	instant; very short period of time (page 18)

stalactites	*noun*	limestone formations that hang from the ceilings of caves (page 38)
stalagmites	*noun*	limestone deposits, resembling icicles, that rise from cave floors (page 38)
statistical	*adjective*	related to numbers that give information about people, places, and things (page 75)
statistics	*noun*	numbers that give facts about people, places, and things (page 74)
storage	*noun*	space to save something for later use (page 104)
surgical	*adjective*	having to do with medical operations (page 48)
symmetry	*noun*	an arrangement of parts in a mirror-like way around a central point or line (page 88)
system	*noun*	network; method; scheme (page 28)
systematic	*adjective*	having an organized method (page 34)

T

technological	*adjective*	having to do with the progress in the use of machinery and automation (page 28)
terminal	*noun*	a depot (page 28)
tragedies	*noun*	disasters; sad events (page 9)
tragic	*adjective*	sad; heartbreaking (page 14)
transformation	*noun*	alteration, change (pages 14, 98)
transformed	*verb*	converted; changed (page 8)
transistors	*noun*	electronic devices that take the place of radio tubes (page 18)
typical	*adjective*	usual (page 59)
typify	*verb*	to be an example of (page 64)

U

unemotional	*adjective*	lacking feelings (page 14)
uninquisitive	*adjective*	lacking curiosity (page 14)
unique	*adjective*	one and only (page 8)
uniqueness	*noun*	the quality of being the one and only (page 14)
universal	*adjective*	worldwide (page 58)
universe	*noun*	the totality of all things that exist in space; the earth and all people (page 64)
unspoiled	*adjective*	not touched or marred; undamaged (page 38)
utility	*adjective*	usefulness (page 24)

V

vagabond	*adjective*	wandering (page 58)
variables	*noun*	changing numbers; symbols that represent things that can change (page 18)
veto	*noun*	the power to prevent a bill from becoming law; rejection (page 59)
volumes	*noun*	quantities; bulks; masses or amounts (page 28)

W

wasteful	*adjective*	using or spending too much (page 74)
wastefulness	*noun*	the unwise use or spending of resources (page 75)

Answer Key

Pages 10–11

1. C	11. D
2. C	12. D
3. D	13. B
4. B	14. C
5. B	15. B
6. B	16. B
7. D	17. A
8. A	18. B
9. D	19. C
10. B	20. D

Page 12

Page 13

1. A
2. B
3. C
4. A
5. D
6. B
7. A
8. D
9. C
10. A
11. C

12. B
13. D
14. C

Page 14

1. inquire
2. humorous
3. memorize
4. devotion
5. association
6. exterior
7. pursuit
8. fiction
9. uniqueness
10. emotion

Page 15

1. B
2. A
3. B
4. C
5. B
6. A

Page 16

The Prefixes *un-* and *non-*

1. B
2. C
3. A
4. E
5. D

The Suffix *-ist*

1. individualist
2. guitarist
3. biologist
4. psychologist
5. revolutionist

Page 17

Answers will vary based on students' personal experiences.

Page 19 *The Navy's Computer Age*

1. adequately

2. split second
3. counterclockwise
4. educator
5. experimental
6. variables
7. application
8. initiative
9. transistors
10. constructive

Page 20
Synonyms and Antonyms
1. Antonyms
2. Synonyms
3. Synonyms
4. Antonyms
5. Synonyms
6. Antonyms
7. Antonyms

Cloze Paragraphs
1. split second
2. counterclockwise
3. initiative
4. constructive
5. educator

Page 21
Across
2. experimental
4. application
6. constructive
7. initiative
8. split second

Down
1. transistors
2. educator
3. adequately
5. variables

Page 22
Word Game
1. transistors
2. educator
3. initiative
4. experimental

5. split second
6. constructive
7. counterclockwise

Challenge Yourself
Answers may vary. Sample answers are provided.
1. blink, sneeze
2. ride a bike, long division
3. Ms. Brown, Mr. Martínez

Page 23
1. D
2. A
3. C
4. A
5. B
6. A
7. C
8. D
9. D
10. A

Page 24
1. automated
2. utility
3. modem
4. revolutionized
5. replacements
6. contemporary
7. integrates
8. outmoded
9. convenience
10. simplifying

Page 25
Word Origins
1. integrates
2. automated
3. simplifying
4. contemporary
5. utility
6. convenience

Word Groups
1. contemporary
2. utility

3. replacements
4. convenience
5. outmoded
6. revolutionized

Page 26
Analogies
1. revolutionized
2. convenience
3. contemporary
4. outmoded
5. modem
6. integrates
7. replacements
8. automated

Word Pairs
Answers may vary. Sample answers are provided.
1. Organizations utilize computers for every aspect of their business.
   The computer's utility has expanded to include entertainment.
2. The pattern for knitting a scarf is simple.
   Simplifying one's life starts with organization.
3. It has become automatic for me to take out the trash on Wednesday before I make breakfast.
   We listened to an automated recording of movie times.

Page 27
Answers will vary based on students' personal experiences.

Pages 30–31   *Moving Oil & Gas*
1. B	11. B
2. C	12. B
3. C	13. A
4. A	14. B
5. B	15. A
6. A	16. D
7. B	17. B
8. C	18. A
9. B	19. D
10. D	20. B

Page 32

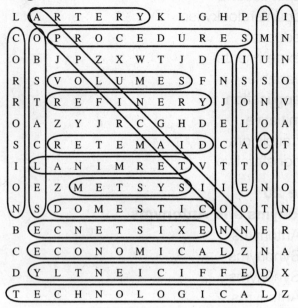

Page 33
1. D
2. A
3. C
4. C
5. C
6. A
7. C
8. A
9. A
10. B
11. D
12. B
13. D
14. D

Page 34
1. isolation
2. systematic
3. consumer
4. refine
5. apply
6. corrosive
7. proceed
8. contention
9. arterial
10. efficiency

Page 35
True-False
1. T
2. F
3. F
4. T
5. T
6. F
7. T
8. F
9. T
10. T

Suffix Additions
1. arterial
2. consumer
3. contention
4. corrosive
5. isolation

Page 36
The Latin Root *jacere*
1. D
2. E
3. A
4. C
5. B

Sentence Completion
1. inject
2. reject
3. dejected
4. project
5. eject

Page 37
Answers will vary based on students' personal experiences.

Page 39
Underground Palace
1. stalactites
2. stalagmites
3. radiated
4. magnificence
5. landscape
6. unspoiled
7. iridescent

8. alcoves
9. speleology
10. features

Page 40
1. speleology
2. alcove
3. landscape
4. features
5. stalactites
6. stalagmites
7. radiated
8. iridescent
9. magnificence
10. unspoiled

Page 41
Word Groups
1. features
2. magnificence
3. alcove
4. landscape
5. iridescent
6. unspoiled

Challenge Yourself
Answers may vary. Sample answers are provided.
1. wings, beaks
2. cactus, sand
3. brilliant, beautiful

Page 42
Word Pairs
Answers may vary. Sample answers are provided.
1. The rays radiate from the sun.
   Heat radiated from the fire.
2. Don't spoil dinner with snacks.
   The unspoiled river was pure and clear.
3. People who love caves study speleology.
   A speleologist would be interested in exploring a newly found cave.
4. We toured a magnificent palace on our vacation.
   We were dazzled by the magnificence of

the scenery.

Forming Words
Answers may vary. Sample answers are provided.

game, fame, fine, mean, mine, fence, gain, fang, mane, name

Page 43
1. C
2. D
3. B
4. A
5. B
6. A
7. D
8. B
9. D
10. C

Page 44
Understanding Related Words
1. analyze
2. immensity
3. cosmos
4. probe
5. inevitable
6. infinite
7. controversial
8. inquiry
9. invaluable
10. ascertain

Name Game
Answers may vary. Sample answers are provided.

1. eating, going to school
2. elephant, giraffe
3. friendship, health
4. what high school will be like, what position I will play next year on the soccer team

Page 45
Dictionary Skills
1. probe
2. cosmos
3. cosmos

4. immensity, inevitable, infinite

Rewriting Sentences
1. My brother's help on this project was invaluable.
2. Once we have all of the information, we will analyze it.
3. The team's decision to elect a captain was controversial.
4. We need to ascertain how many people are coming to dinner.

Page 46
1. D
2. B
3. B
4. C
5. A
6. D
7. B
8. A
9. D
10. B

Page 47
Answers will vary based on students' personal experiences.

Page 49 Triumph & Tragedy
1. hospitalized
2. clinical
3. diagnosis
4. surgical
5. optimistic
6. affliction, consolation
7. paralytic
8. neurology
9. pediatrician

Page 50
Medical Words
1. hospitalized
2. neurology
3. clinical
4. pediatrician
5. surgical
6. paralytic

7. diagnosis

Writing Sentences

Answers may vary. Sample answers are provided.

1. The doctor told me about my affliction.
2. Because she was interested in the nervous system, she studied neurology.
3. It was little consolation to the team to learn their main rival lost the finals.
4. The doctor's clinical knowledge made him a good choice.
5. She was optimistic her patient would make a full recovery.
6. This pediatrician sees teenagers as well as young children.

Page 51

Answers may vary. Sample answers are provided. Vocabulary words are italicized.

Kinds of Doctors

1. *pediatrician*
2. *surgical* doctor (or surgeon)
3. neurologist
4. cardiologist
5. psychologist

What a Doctor Needs to Be

1. *optimistic*
2. smart
3. kind
4. patient
5 thorough

Problems or Conditions They Treat

1. *afflictions*
2. *paralytic*
3. sore throat
4. cold
5. broken foot

What Doctors Do

1. *diagnosis*
2. surgery
3. read charts
4. treat illnesses
5. ask questions

Page 52
Synonyms and Antonyms

1. Synonyms
2. Antonyms
3. Synonyms
4. Synonyms
5. Antonyms

The Suffixes –ician and –ist

1. beautician
2. biologist
3. statistician
4. artist
5. typist
6. musician
7. chemist
8. speleologist

Page 53

1. D
2. A
3. B
4. B
5. D
6. C
7. D
8. D
9. D
10. A

Page 54

1. inadequate
2. lethal
3. devastate
4. contributor
5. seismic
6. evaluate
7. accuracy
8. compute
9. anticipate
10. avert

Page 55
Word Groups

1. lethal
2. devastate
3. anticipate

4. compute
5. contributor
6. evaluate

Dictionary Skills
1. inadequate, B
2. anticipate, A
3. contributor, A
4. accuracy, B
5. avert, B

Page 56
1. inadequate
2. anticipate
3. contributor
4. devastate
5. lethal
6. accuracy
7. seismic
8. evaluate
9. compute
10. averted

Page 57
Answers will vary based on students' personal experiences.

Pages 60–61   *Thomas Edison*
1. C   2. A
3. B   4. A
5. B   6. C
7. B   8. D
9. C   10. B
11. D   12. A
13. C   14. C
15. A   16. B
17. C   18. D
19. B   20. A

Page 62
1. c
2. b
3. a
4. b
5. a
6. b
7. c

8. d
9. b
10. a

Page 63
1. D
2. A
3. B
4. C
5. A
6. B
7. A
8. A
9. A
10. A
11. D
12. B
13. D
14. C

Page 64
1. require
2. inquire
3. monopoly
4. defective
5. acquisition
6. prominence
7. achieve
8. maintain
9. duplication
10. typify

Page 65
1. include, exclude
2. typical, atypical
3. finance, financier
4. eligibility, ineligible
5. despair, desperation
6. achieve, achievement

Page 66
The Latin Root *uni*
1. uniform
2. unicycle
3. unit
4. united
5. universe

The Greek Root *mono*

1. monarch
2. monotony
3. monoplane
4. monorail
5. monotone

Page 67

Answers will vary based on students' personal experiences.

Page 69

Food into Energy

1. deficiency
2. consume
3. nutrients
4. digestion
5. carbohydrates
6. calories
7. malnutrition
8. enzymes
9. absorption
10. proteins

Page 70

Rewriting Sentences

1. He follows a diet low in carbohydrates.
2. Enzymes help your body digest food.
3. To lose weight, you must exercise more and consume less food.
4. The doctor found that the child suffered from malnutrition.

Cloze Paragraphs

1. nutrients
2. consume
3. calories
4. deficiency
5. carbohydrates
6. protein
7. digestion
8. absorption

Page 71

1. nutrients
2. proteins
3. carbohydrates
4. consume

5. calories
6. digestion
7. enzymes
8. deficiency
9. malnutrition
10. absorption

Page 72

Word Game

1. consume
2. absorption
3. enzymes
4. calories
5. malnutrition
6. nutrients

Challenge Yourself

Answers may vary. Sample answers are provided.

1. candy, bread
2. fish, beef, chicken
3. eating the wrong foods; not eating enough food

Page 73

1. A
2. C
3. A
4. C
5. A
6. B
7. B
8. C
9. D
10. A

Page 74

1. wasteful
2. complexity
3. replenished
4. statistics
5. commodity
6. geothermal
7. compensate
8. discretion
9. conversion

10. conservationists

Page 75
Analogies
1. geothermal
2. replenished
3. conversion
4. commodity
5. conservationists

Word Pairs
Answers may vary. Sample answers are provided.

1. The movie stars have to be discreet so that the press doesn't see them leave the restaurant.
   It is important to use discretion when making a decision and not act without having all the information.
2. The mother promised to compensate her children for their time by giving them extra allowance.
   It is important to ask about compensation before applying for a job.
3. It is wasteful to throw away perfectly good food.
   Her wastefulness cost a lot of money because we had to buy extra groceries.
4. Psychologists use statistics when they perform studies.
   Statistical analysis shows that most people support the president.
5. The complex math problem challenged the students, but they were able to solve it.
   The complexity of the digestive system is well understood by biologists.

Page 76
1. compensate
2. wasteful
3. replenished
4. conservationist
5. geothermal
6. conversion
7. discretion
8. complexity
9. statistics

10. commodity

Page 77
Answers will vary based on students' personal experiences.

Page 79   *Triangle of Mystery*
1. acknowledge
2. perplexed
3. coincidental
4. bizarre
5. perceptions
6. circumstances
7. speculate
8. phenomenon
9. oceanographic
10. mystical

Page 80
Analogies
1. mystical
2. bizarre
3. acknowledge
4. speculate

Cloze Paragraphs
1. phenomenon
2. circumstances
3. speculated
4. bizarre
5. perplexed
6. mystical

Page 81
Word Pairs
Answers may vary. Sample answers are provided.

1. It is perplexing to many people that violent movies are popular.
   I am perplexed by my math homework, so I am going to ask for help.
2. The detective noted the odd circumstances surrounding the man's disappearance.
   There was only circumstantial evidence linking her to the crime.
3. Their birthdays coincide, so they celebrate

each year at a different restaurant.
Meeting my friend at the mall was entirely
coincidental.

4. A strange phenomenon has been sighted in the woods by our house.
The performance was phenomenal—no one has ever put on a show like that before!

5. I acknowledge that you have a good point, but I still disagree with your basic ideas.
The old woman sent a note as acknowledgement of the young boy's good deed.

6. Because I love everything about the ocean, I am going to study oceanography.
The oceanographic sciences will help us learn more about the creatures of the ocean.

7. Our perceptions of the event were all different.
People do perceive things differently, sometimes depending on their mood.

Page 82
The Latin Root *spec*
1. spectator
2. specimen
3. specter
4. spectacles
5. speculative

Challenge Yourself
Answers may vary. Sample answers are provided.
1. tides, whales
2. rain, not doing chores
3. when I borrowed my sister's sweater without asking; when I picked up the wrong backpack at soccer practice

Page 83
1. B
2. A
3. B
4. B
5. A
6. D

7. D
8. A
9. C
10. D

Page 84
1. brink
2. interior
3. receded
4. protrude
5. plateau
6. erosion
7. embedded
8. clefts
9. chasm
10. desolate

Page 85
Word Origins
1. plateau
2. erosion
3. cleft
4. recede
5. desolate
6. protrude
7. chasm

Using Analogies
1. brink
2. interior
3. chasm
4. plateau
5. recede

Page 86
1. A
2. C
3. B
4. C
5. D
6. B
7. B
8. D
9. A
10. B

Page 87

Answers will vary based on students' personal experiences.

Page 89 *Puzzle Built of Stones*

1. sightseers
2. intact
3. radiocarbon
4. revelations
5. imply
6. solstice
7. alignment
8. symmetry
9. rites
10. astrology

Page 90

1. sightseers
2. intact
3. alignment
4. solstice
5. symmetry
6. imply
7. rites
8. astrology
9. radiocarbon
10. revelations

Page 91
Analogies

1. imply
2. intact
3. astrology
4. sightseers
5. revelations

Rewriting Sentences

1. I visited Stonehenge on the solstice.
2. We were told by a guide that the symmetry of the stones may have made it possible for ancient Britons to predict eclipses.
3. The stone altar may have served for rites relating to astrology.

Page 92
Figures of Speech

1. personification
2. simile or personification
3. simile
4. personification
5. simile

Word Groups

1. intact
2. sightseers
3. symmetry
4. revelations
5. imply

Page 93

1. A
2. B
3. C
4. C
5. B
6. D
7. C
8. B
9. B
10. D

Page 94

1. archaeologists
2. excavate
3. bonanza
4. cultural
5. characteristic
6. frequency
7. descriptive
8. engravings
9. reverence
10. continuity

Page 95
Using Analogies

1. characteristic
2. bonanza
3. reverence
4. archaeologists
5. excavate
6. engravings

7. continuity

Cloze Paragraph
1. archaeologists
2. engravings
3. descriptive
4. cultural
5. frequency
6. continuity

Page 96
1. C
2. C
3. B
4. B
5. D
6. B
7. A
8. D
9. A
10. D

Page 97
Answers will vary based on students' personal experiences.

Page 99   *Photographs of the Future*
1. identification
2. criminology
3. projection
4. envision
5. alterations
6. transformation
7. components
8. primarily
9. despite
10. dilemma

Page 100
Word Groups
1. dilemma
2. alterations
3. components
4. envision

Rewriting Sentences
1. The use of computers in criminology is helpful.
2. Computer art can help to provide identification, after that person has gone through physical changes.
3. Within a few seconds, a photo of a child can undergo a transformation.
4. Although the image created is only a projection, it seems that the changes are often quite accurate.

Page 101
Across
2. despite
6. components
8. primarily
9. criminology
10. projection

Down
1. identification
3. envision
4. dilemma
5. alterations
7. transformation

Page 102
Word Game
1. dilemma
2. primarily
3. identification
4. criminology
5. transformation
6. alterations

Challenge Yourself
Answers may vary. Sample answers are provided.
1. school ID, birth certificate
2. kitten growing into a cat
3. I'm saving money for new music by renting DVDs instead of going to the movies.

Page 103
1. C
2. B
3. D
4. A

www.harcourtschoolsupply.com
© HMH Supplemental Publishers Inc. All rights reserved.

127

Answer Key
Vocabulary in Context G8, SV 9780547625812

5. A
6. A
7. B
8. A
9. C
10. D

Page 104

1. automatically
2. storage
3. access
4. electronic
5. limitless
6. capability
7. monitor
8. quantity
9. manipulate
10. alternative

Page 105
Synonyms

1. capability
2. limitless
3. monitor
4. quantity
5. manipulate

Cloze Paragraph

1. access
2. automatically
3. alternatives
4. storage
5. electronic

Page 106

Answers may vary. Sample answers are provided. Vocabulary words are italicized.

How Computers Operate

1. *automatically*
2. *electronic*
3. *access*
4. quickly
5. networks

What Computers Do

1. *storage*

2. word processing
3. photographs
4. multimedia
5. information

How Computers Work Better Than People

1. *limitless*
2. *capability*
3. *quantity*
4. faster
5. remember a lot

Subjects of Computer Games

1. aliens
2. bowling
3. tennis
4. auto racing
5. football

Page 107

Answers will vary based on students' personal experiences.

Vocabulary in Context G8, SV 9780547625812